Take It to Your Seat Centers

Reading & Language

6

Using the Centers

The centers in this book are intended for skill practice and reinforcement, not as an introduction to skills. It is important to model the use of each center before students are asked to do the tasks independently.

Why Use Centers?

- Centers are a motivating way for students to practice important skills.

- They appeal especially to kinesthetic and visual learners.

- The 12 centers in this book are self-contained and portable. Students can work at a desk, at a table, or on a rug.

- Once you've made the centers, they're ready to use at any time.

Before Using Centers

You and your students will enjoy using the centers more if you think through logistical considerations. Here are a few questions to resolve ahead of time:

- Will students select a center, or will you assign the centers and use them as a skill assessment tool?

- Will there be a specific block of time for centers, or will the centers be used throughout the day as students complete other work?

- Where will you place the centers for easy access by students?

- What procedure will students use when they need help with the center tasks?

- Will students use the answer key to check their own work?

- How will you use the center checklist to track student completion of the centers?

A Place for Centers

Make the centers ahead of time so that they are ready for student use whenever specific skill practice is indicated.

Store the prepared centers in a filing box or crate. If you wish the centers to be self-checking, include the answer key with the center materials.

Introducing the Centers

Use the student direction cover page to review the skill to be practiced.

Read each step to the students and model what to do, showing students the center pieces.

Record Progress

Use the center checklist (page 4) to record the date and student achievement.

Making the Centers

Included in Each Center

(A) Student direction cover page

(B) Task cards and/or mats

(C) Reproducible student response form

(D) Answer key

Materials Needed

- Colored file folders with inside pockets

- Small envelopes or plastic self-closing bags (for storing cut task cards)

- Pencils and marking pens (for labeling envelopes)

- Scissors

- Double-sided tape

- Laminated center pieces

- Answer key pages

Steps to Follow

1. Tape the student direction page to the front of the file folder.

2. Place the reproduced response forms in the left-hand pocket.

3. Laminate the task cards and mats. Put the cut cards in a labeled envelope or plastic self-closing bag. Place the mats and task cards in the right-hand pocket of the file folder.

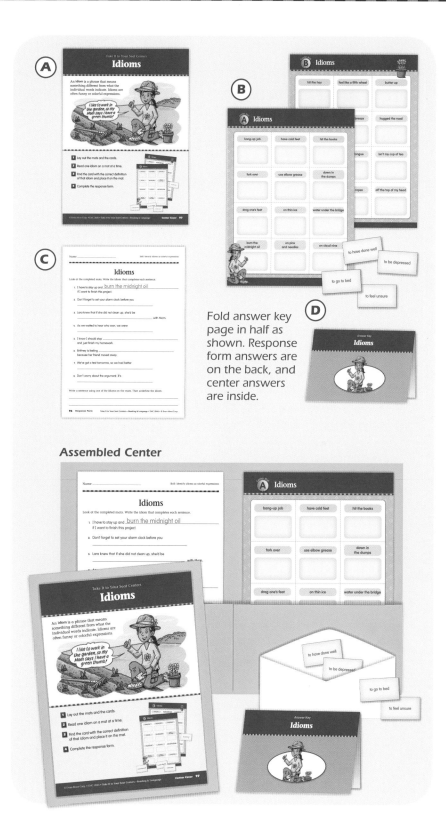

Fold answer key page in half as shown. Response form answers are on the back, and center answers are inside.

Assembled Center

Center Checklist

Center / Skills	Skill Level	Date
1. Synonyms/Antonyms Distinguish if a pair of words are synonyms or antonyms		
2. Homophones Identify the correct homophone to use in a sentence		
3. Homographs Identify the multiple meanings of homographs		
4. Greek and Latin Roots Recognize word roots originating in other languages		
5. Prefixes Identify prefixes as word parts added to the beginning of a base word that change the meaning of that word		
6. Suffixes Identify suffixes as word parts added to the end of a base word that change the meaning and part of speech of that word		
7. Analogies Identify analogies as a kind of comparison		
8. Idioms Identify idioms as colorful expressions		
9. Similes and Metaphors Distinguish between a metaphor and a simile		
10. Using Context Clues Use context clues to help define unfamiliar vocabulary in a reading selection		
11. Inference Use clues in a reading passage to understand what is being implied		
12. Main Idea and Details Identify the main idea and supporting details in a reading passage		

Synonyms/ Antonyms

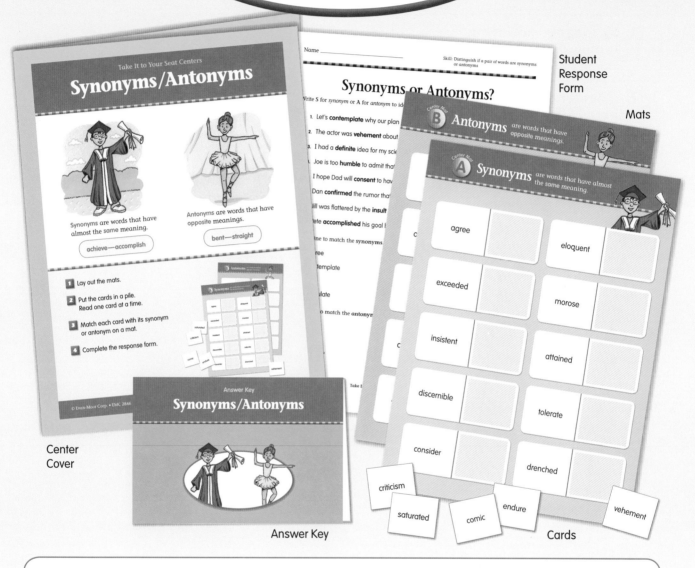

Center Cover

Answer Key

Cards

Student Response Form

Mats

Skill
Distinguish if a pair of words are synonyms or antonyms

Prepare the Center
Follow the directions on page 3.

Introduce the Center
Demonstrate how to use the center. State the goal: *You will read each word card and place it next to its synonym or antonym on the mat.*

Synonyms or Antonyms?

Write **S** for *synonym* or **A** for *antonym* to identify each pair of bold words.

1. Let's **contemplate** why our plan didn't work. **(consider)**   _S_

2. The actor was **vehement** about having his own room. **(insistent)**   _____

3. I had a **definite** idea for my science project. **(vague)**   _____

4. Joe is too **humble** to admit that he doesn't know everything. **(arrogant)**   _____

5. I hope Dad will **consent** to having ice cream for dessert! **(agree)**   _____

6. Dan **confirmed** the rumor that it was his birthday. **(denied)**   _____

7. Jill was flattered by the **insult** about her shoes. **(compliment)**   _____

8. Pete **accomplished** his goal by practicing daily. **(attained)**   _____

Draw a line to match the **synonyms**.

agree	• morose
contemplate	• eloquent
sad	• consent
articulate	• consider

Draw a line to match the **antonyms**.

rigid	• doubt
insult	• compliment
certainty	• arrogant
humble	• flexible

Synonyms/Antonyms

Synonyms are words that have almost the **same** meaning.

achieve—accomplish

Antonyms are words that have **opposite** meanings.

bent—straight

1 Lay out the mats.

2 Put the cards in a pile.
Read one card at a time.

3 Match each card with its synonym or antonym on a mat.

4 Complete the response form.

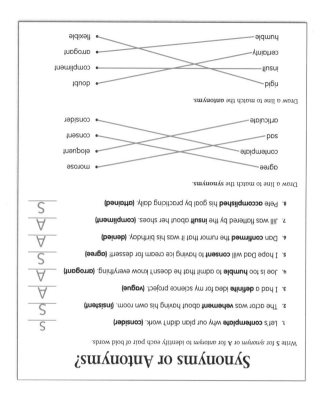

Synonyms or Antonyms?

Write *S* for *synonym* or *A* for *antonym* to identify each pair of bold words.

1. Let's **contemplate** why our plan didn't work. (**consider**) — S
2. The actor was **vehement** about having his own room. (**insistent**) — S
3. I had a **definite** idea for my science project. (**vague**) — A
4. Joe is too **humble** to admit that he doesn't know everything. (**arrogant**) — A
5. I hope Dad will **consent** to having ice cream for dessert! (**agree**) — S
6. Dan **confirmed** the rumor that it was his birthday. (**denied**) — A
7. Jill was flattered by the **insult** about her shoes. (**compliment**) — A
8. Pete **accomplished** his goal by practicing daily. (**attained**) — S

Draw a line to match the synonyms.

- morose — agree
- eloquent — contemplate
- consent — sad
- consider — articulate

Draw a line to match the antonyms.

- doubt — rigid
- compliment — insult
- arrogant — certainty
- flexible — humble

Response Form

(fold)

Answer Key

Synonyms/Antonyms

Answer Key
Synonyms/Antonyms

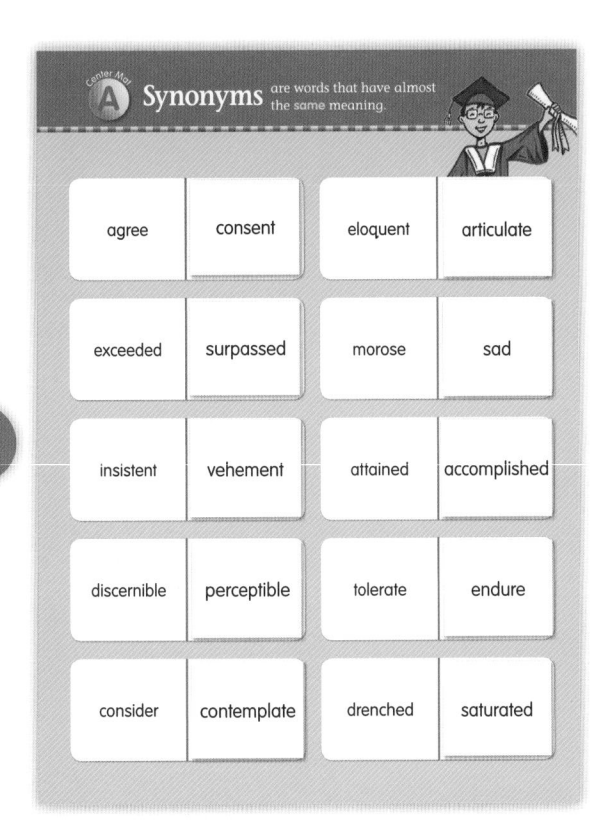

Synonyms are words that have almost the same meaning.

agree / consent	eloquent / articulate
exceeded / surpassed	morose / sad
insistent / vehement	attained / accomplished
discernible / perceptible	tolerate / endure
consider / contemplate	drenched / saturated

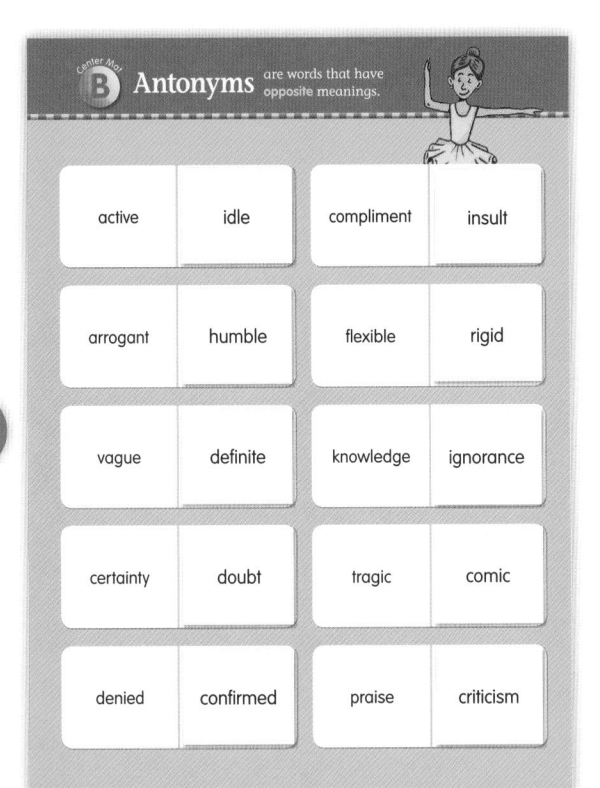

Antonyms are words that have opposite meanings.

active / idle	compliment / insult
arrogant / humble	flexible / rigid
vague / definite	knowledge / ignorance
certainty / doubt	tragic / comic
denied / confirmed	praise / criticism

Center Mat

A **Synonyms** are words that have almost the **same** meaning.

agree	

eloquent	

exceeded	

morose	

insistent	

attained	

discernible	

tolerate	

consider	

drenched	

active	

compliment	

arrogant	

flexible	

vague	

knowledge	

certainty	

tragic	

denied	

praise	

contemplate	vehement	consent	accomplished
sad	surpassed	articulate	perceptible
endure	saturated	confirmed	insult
definite	idle	rigid	humble
doubt	ignorance	comic	criticism

Synonyms/Antonyms	Synonyms/Antonyms	Synonyms/Antonyms	Synonyms/Antonyms
Take It to Your Seat Centers Reading & Language EMC 2846 © Evan-Moor Corp.	Take It to Your Seat Centers Reading & Language EMC 2846 © Evan-Moor Corp.	Take It to Your Seat Centers Reading & Language EMC 2846 © Evan-Moor Corp.	Take It to Your Seat Centers Reading & Language EMC 2846 © Evan-Moor Corp.
Synonyms/Antonyms	Synonyms/Antonyms	Synonyms/Antonyms	Synonyms/Antonyms
Take It to Your Seat Centers Reading & Language EMC 2846 © Evan-Moor Corp.	Take It to Your Seat Centers Reading & Language EMC 2846 © Evan-Moor Corp.	Take It to Your Seat Centers Reading & Language EMC 2846 © Evan-Moor Corp.	Take It to Your Seat Centers Reading & Language EMC 2846 © Evan-Moor Corp.
Synonyms/Antonyms	Synonyms/Antonyms	Synonyms/Antonyms	Synonyms/Antonyms
Take It to Your Seat Centers Reading & Language EMC 2846 © Evan-Moor Corp.	Take It to Your Seat Centers Reading & Language EMC 2846 © Evan-Moor Corp.	Take It to Your Seat Centers Reading & Language EMC 2846 © Evan-Moor Corp.	Take It to Your Seat Centers Reading & Language EMC 2846 © Evan-Moor Corp.
Synonyms/Antonyms	Synonyms/Antonyms	Synonyms/Antonyms	Synonyms/Antonyms
Take It to Your Seat Centers Reading & Language EMC 2846 © Evan-Moor Corp.	Take It to Your Seat Centers Reading & Language EMC 2846 © Evan-Moor Corp.	Take It to Your Seat Centers Reading & Language EMC 2846 © Evan-Moor Corp.	Take It to Your Seat Centers Reading & Language EMC 2846 © Evan-Moor Corp.
Synonyms/Antonyms	Synonyms/Antonyms	Synonyms/Antonyms	Synonyms/Antonyms
Take It to Your Seat Centers Reading & Language EMC 2846 © Evan-Moor Corp.	Take It to Your Seat Centers Reading & Language EMC 2846 © Evan-Moor Corp.	Take It to Your Seat Centers Reading & Language EMC 2846 © Evan-Moor Corp.	Take It to Your Seat Centers Reading & Language EMC 2846 © Evan-Moor Corp.

Homophones

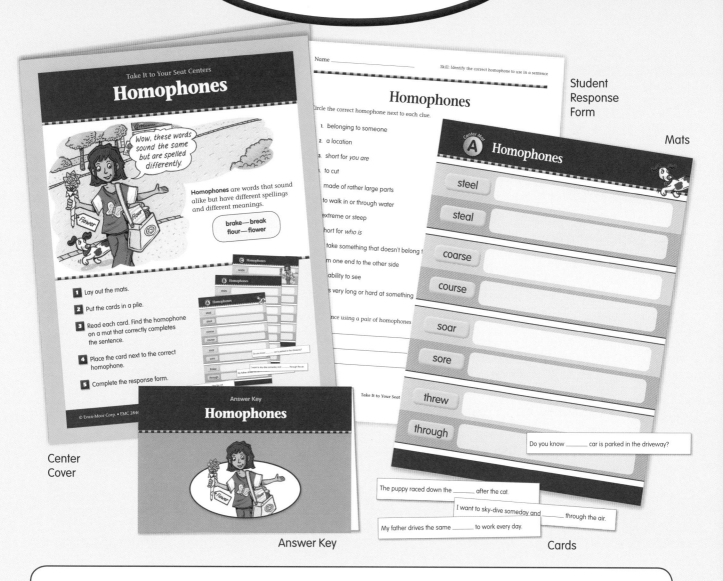

Center Cover

Student Response Form

Answer Key

Mats

Cards

Skill
Identify the correct homophone to use in a sentence

Prepare the Center
Follow the directions on page 3.

Introduce the Center
Demonstrate how the center works. State the goal: *You will read each sentence card containing a missing homophone and place it beside the correct homophone on the mat.*

Homophones

Circle the correct homophone next to each clue.

1. belonging to someone   who's   (whose)
2. a location   site   sight
3. short for *you are*   your   you're
4. to cut   shear   sheer
5. made of rather large parts   course   coarse
6. to walk in or through water   wade   weighed
7. extreme or steep   sheer   shear
8. short for *who is*   who's   whose
9. to take something that doesn't belong to you   steel   steal
10. from one end to the other side   threw   through
11. the ability to see   site   sight
12. looks very long or hard at something   stares   stairs

Write a sentence using a pair of homophones from above.

_____

_____

_____

Homophones

Wow, these words sound the same but are spelled differently.

Homophones are words that sound alike but have different spellings and different meanings.

> brake—break
> flour—flower

1 Lay out the mats.

2 Put the cards in a pile.

3 Read each card. Find the homophone on a mat that correctly completes the sentence.

4 Place the card next to the correct homophone.

5 Complete the response form.

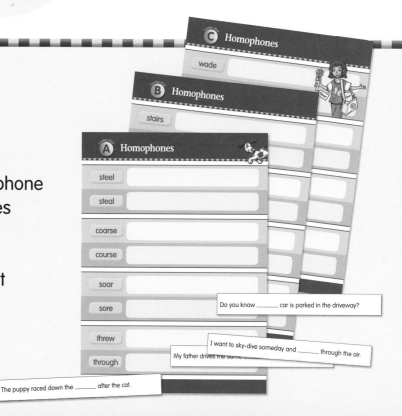

Homophones

Answer Key

(fold)

Response Form

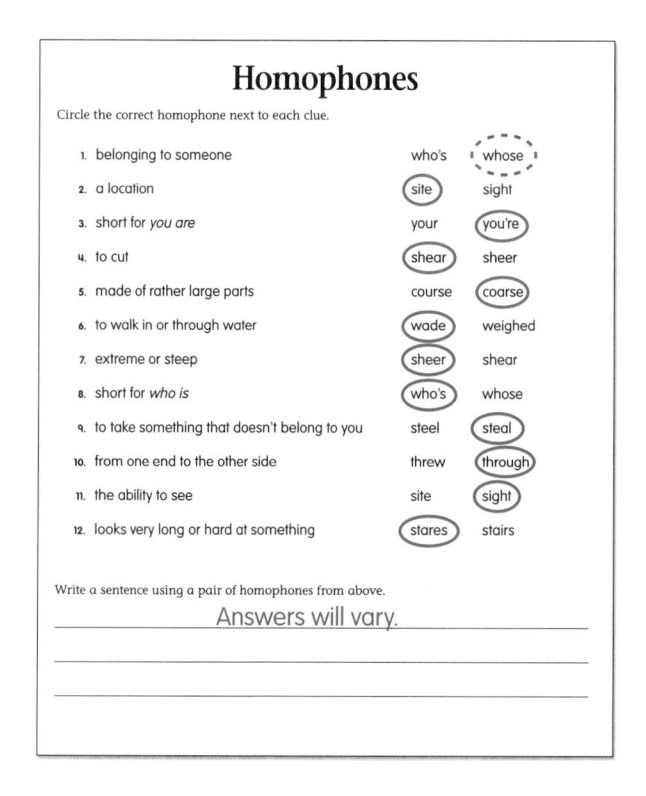

Homophones

Circle the correct homophone next to each clue.

1.	belonging to someone	who's	**(whose)**
2.	a location	**(site)**	sight
3.	short for *you are*	your	**(you're)**
4.	to cut	**(shear)**	sheer
5.	made of rather large parts	course	**(coarse)**
6.	to walk in or through water	**(wade)**	weighed
7.	extreme or steep	**(sheer)**	shear
8.	short for *who is*	**(who's)**	whose
9.	to take something that doesn't belong to you	steel	**(steal)**
10.	from one end to the other side	threw	**(through)**
11.	the ability to see	site	**(sight)**
12.	looks very long or hard at something	**(stares)**	stairs

Write a sentence using a pair of homophones from above.

Answers will vary.

Answer Key
Homophones

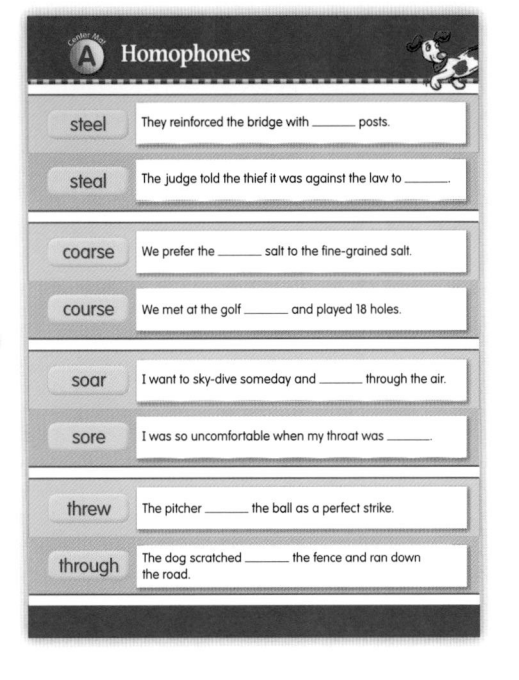

A Homophones

steel	They reinforced the bridge with _____ posts.
steal	The judge told the thief it was against the law to _____.
coarse	We prefer the _____ salt to the fine-grained salt.
course	We met at the golf _____ and played 18 holes.
soar	I want to sky-dive someday and _____ through the air.
sore	I was so uncomfortable when my throat was _____.
threw	The pitcher _____ the ball as a perfect strike.
through	The dog scratched _____ the fence and ran down the road.

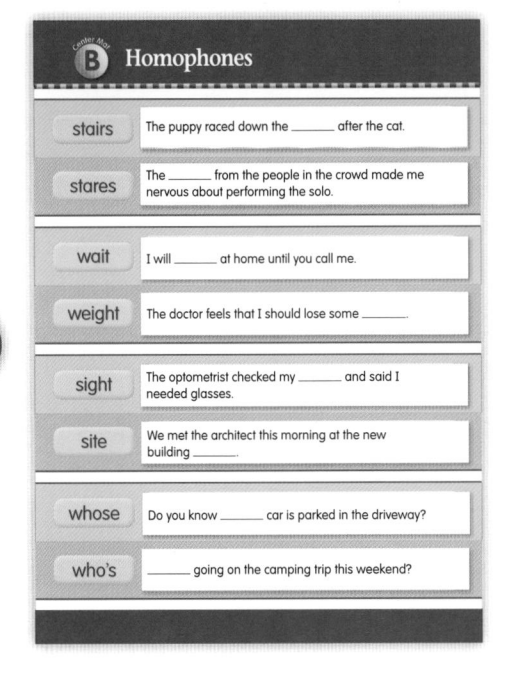

B Homophones

stairs	The puppy raced down the _____ after the cat.
stares	The _____ from the people in the crowd made me nervous about performing the solo.
wait	I will _____ at home until you call me.
weight	The doctor feels that I should lose some _____.
sight	The optometrist checked my _____ and said I needed glasses.
site	We met the architect this morning at the new building _____.
whose	Do you know _____ car is parked in the driveway?
who's	_____ going on the camping trip this weekend?

C Homophones

wade	My friends and I love to go to the beach and _____ in the water.
weighed	The professional boxer _____ in at 160 pounds.
your	I found _____ backpack in the garage yesterday.
you're	If _____ going to camp this summer, we can be roommates.
sheer	Did you see the parasailor jump off the _____ side of the cliff?
shear	My dad needs to _____ the hedge so we can open the garage door.
root	A plant's _____ ball absorbs the necessary nutrients from the soil.
route	My father drives the same _____ to work every day.

steel

steal

coarse

course

soar

sore

threw

through

Center Mat

B Homophones

| stairs | |
| stares | |

| wait | |
| weight | |

| sight | |
| site | |

| whose | |
| who's | |

Homophones

Center Mat

C

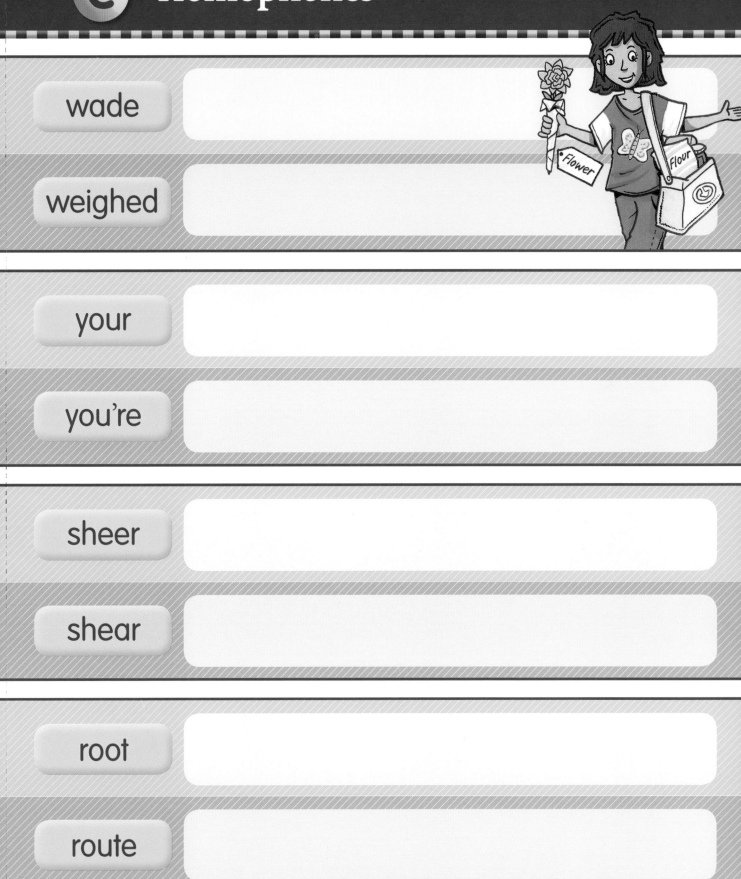

wade

weighed

your

you're

sheer

shear

root

route

They reinforced the bridge with _____ posts.

The judge told the thief it was against the law to _____.

We met at the golf _____ and played 18 holes.

We prefer the _____ salt to the fine-grained salt.

I was so uncomfortable when my throat was _____.

I want to sky-dive someday and _____ through the air.

The pitcher _____ the ball as a perfect strike.

The dog scratched _____ the fence and ran down the road.

The _____ from the people in the crowd made me nervous about performing the solo.

The puppy raced down the _____ after the cat.

I will _____ at home until you call me.

The doctor feels that I should lose some _____.

Homophones

Take It to Your Seat Centers—Reading & Language
EMC 2846 • © Evan-Moor Corp.

Homophones

Take It to Your Seat Centers—Reading & Language
EMC 2846 • © Evan-Moor Corp.

Homophones

Take It to Your Seat Centers—Reading & Language
EMC 2846 • © Evan-Moor Corp.

Homophones

Take It to Your Seat Centers—Reading & Language
EMC 2846 • © Evan-Moor Corp.

Homophones

Take It to Your Seat Centers—Reading & Language
EMC 2846 • © Evan-Moor Corp.

Homophones

Take It to Your Seat Centers—Reading & Language
EMC 2846 • © Evan-Moor Corp.

Homophones

Take It to Your Seat Centers—Reading & Language
EMC 2846 • © Evan-Moor Corp.

Homophones

Take It to Your Seat Centers—Reading & Language
EMC 2846 • © Evan-Moor Corp.

Homophones

Take It to Your Seat Centers—Reading & Language
EMC 2846 • © Evan-Moor Corp.

Homophones

Take It to Your Seat Centers—Reading & Language
EMC 2846 • © Evan-Moor Corp.

Homophones

Take It to Your Seat Centers—Reading & Language
EMC 2846 • © Evan-Moor Corp.

Homophones

Take It to Your Seat Centers—Reading & Language
EMC 2846 • © Evan-Moor Corp.

We met the architect this morning at the new building _____.

My dad needs to _____ the hedge so we can open the garage door.

The optometrist checked my _____ and said I needed glasses.

Did you see the parasailor jump off the _____ side of the cliff?

Do you know _____ car is parked in the driveway?

A plant's _____ ball absorbs the necessary nutrients from the soil.

_____ going on the camping trip this weekend?

My father drives the same _____ to work every day.

I found _____ backpack in the garage yesterday.

My friends and I love to go to the beach and _____ in the water.

If _____ going to camp this summer, we can be roommates.

The professional boxer _____ in at 160 pounds.

Homophones

Take It to Your Seat Centers—Reading & Language
EMC 2846 • © Evan-Moor Corp.

Homophones

Take It to Your Seat Centers—Reading & Language
EMC 2846 • © Evan-Moor Corp.

Homophones

Take It to Your Seat Centers—Reading & Language
EMC 2846 • © Evan-Moor Corp.

Homophones

Take It to Your Seat Centers—Reading & Language
EMC 2846 • © Evan-Moor Corp.

Homophones

Take It to Your Seat Centers—Reading & Language
EMC 2846 • © Evan-Moor Corp.

Homophones

Take It to Your Seat Centers—Reading & Language
EMC 2846 • © Evan-Moor Corp.

Homophones

Take It to Your Seat Centers—Reading & Language
EMC 2846 • © Evan-Moor Corp.

Homophones

Take It to Your Seat Centers—Reading & Language
EMC 2846 • © Evan-Moor Corp.

Homophones

Take It to Your Seat Centers—Reading & Language
EMC 2846 • © Evan-Moor Corp.

Homophones

Take It to Your Seat Centers—Reading & Language
EMC 2846 • © Evan-Moor Corp.

Homophones

Take It to Your Seat Centers—Reading & Language
EMC 2846 • © Evan-Moor Corp.

Homophones

Take It to Your Seat Centers—Reading & Language
EMC 2846 • © Evan-Moor Corp.

Take It to Your Seat Centers

Homographs

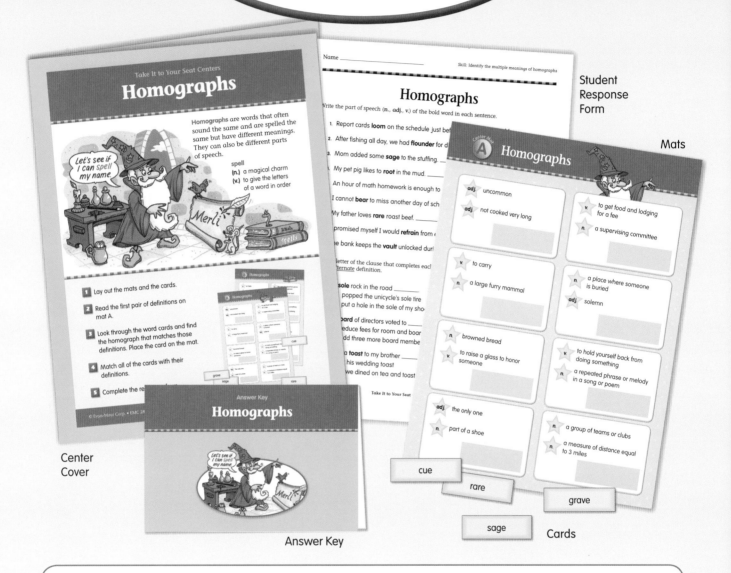

Student Response Form

Mats

Center Cover

Answer Key

Cards

Skill
Identify the multiple meanings of homographs

Prepare the Center
Follow the directions on page 3.

Introduce the Center
Demonstrate how the center works. State the goal: *You will read each pair of definitions on the mats and place the correct homograph card below the definitions.*

Homographs

Write the part of speech (**n.**, **adj.**, **v.**) of the bold word in each sentence.

1. Report cards **loom** on the schedule just before winter break. ___V.___

2. After fishing all day, we had **flounder** for dinner. _____

3. Mom added some **sage** to the stuffing. _____

4. My pet pig likes to **root** in the mud. _____

5. An hour of math homework is enough to make my brain **reel**. _____

6. I cannot **bear** to miss another day of school. _____

7. My father loves **rare** roast beef. _____

8. I promised myself I would **refrain** from eating cookies before dinner. _____

9. The bank keeps the **vault** unlocked during business hours. _____

Write the letter of the clause that completes each sentence and uses a homograph with an <u>alternate</u> definition.

1. The **sole** rock in the road _____.
   a. popped the unicycle's sole tire
   b. put a hole in the sole of my shoe

2. The **board** of directors voted to _____.
   a. reduce fees for room and board
   b. add three more board members

3. I made a **toast** to my brother _____.
   a. for his wedding toast
   b. as we dined on tea and toast

Homographs

Homographs are words that often sound the same and are spelled the same but have different meanings. They can also be different parts of speech.

spell
(n.) a magical charm
(v.) to give the letters of a word in order

1. Lay out the mats and the cards.

2. Read the first pair of definitions on mat A.

3. Look through the word cards and find the homograph that matches those definitions. Place the card on the mat.

4. Match all of the cards with their definitions.

5. Complete the response form.

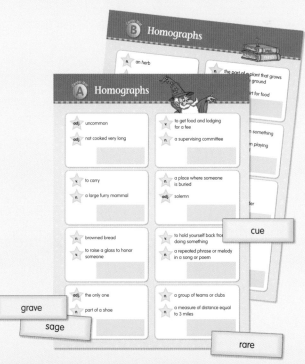

Response Form

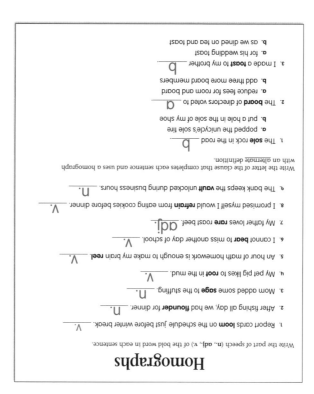

Homographs

Write the part of speech (**n.**, **adj.**, **v.**) of the bold word in each sentence.

1. Report cards **loom** on the schedule just before winter break.   v.
2. After fishing all day, we had **flounder** for dinner.   n.
3. Mom added some **sage** to the stuffing.   n.
4. My pet pig likes to **root** in the mud.   v.
5. An hour of math homework is enough to make my brain **reel**.   v.
6. I cannot **bear** to miss another day of school.   v.
7. My father loves **rare** roast beef.   adj.
8. I promised myself I would **refrain** from eating cookies before dinner.   v.
9. The bank keeps the **vault** unlocked during business hours.   n.

Write the letter of the clause that completes each sentence and uses a homograph with an alternate definition.

1. The **sole** rock in the road _____   b
   a. popped the unicycle's sole tire
   b. put a hole in the sole of my shoe

2. The **board** of directors voted to _____   a
   a. reduce fees for room and board
   b. add three more board members

3. I made a **toast** to my brother _____   b
   a. for his wedding toast
   b. as we dined on tea and toast

(fold)

Answer Key

Homographs

Answer Key

Homographs

Homographs — B

flounder
- v. to struggle clumsily
- n. a marine flatfish

vault
- n. a safe or a tomb
- v. to leap or spring

reel
- v. to stagger or whirl
- n. a device for winding string

hamper
- v. to hold back or hinder
- n. a basket

loom
- v. to appear in front of, looking big or scary
- n. a frame for weaving

cue
- n. a stick used when playing the game of pool
- n. a signal to begin something

sage
- adj. wise
- n. an herb

root
- v. to dig in the dirt for food
- n. the part of a plant that grows down into the ground

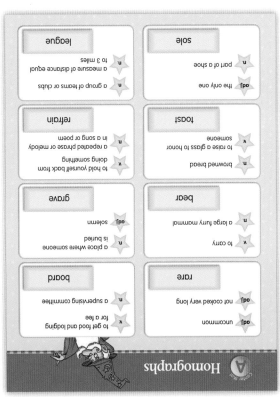

Homographs — A

sole
- n. part of a shoe
- adj. the only one

league
- n. a measure of distance equal to 3 miles
- n. a group of teams or clubs

toast
- v. to raise a glass to honor someone
- n. browned bread

refrain
- n. a repeated phrase or melody in a song or poem
- v. to hold yourself back from doing something

bear
- v. to carry
- n. a large furry mammal

grave
- adj. solemn
- n. a place where someone is buried

rare
- adj. not cooked very long
- adj. uncommon

board
- v. to get food and lodging for a fee
- n. a supervising committee

adj. uncommon

adj. not cooked very long

v. to get food and lodging for a fee

n. a supervising committee

v. to carry

n. a large furry mammal

n. a place where someone is buried

adj. solemn

n. browned bread

v. to raise a glass to honor someone

v. to hold yourself back from doing something

n. a repeated phrase or melody in a song or poem

adj. the only one

n. part of a shoe

n. a group of teams or clubs

n. a measure of distance equal to 3 miles

n. an herb

adj. wise

---

n. the part of a plant that grows down into the ground

v. to dig in the dirt for food

---

n. a frame for weaving

v. to appear in front of, looking big or scary

---

n. a signal to begin something

n. a stick used when playing the game of pool

---

n. a device for winding string

v. to stagger or whirl

---

n. a basket

v. to hold back or hinder

---

n. a marine flatfish

v. to struggle clumsily

---

v. to leap or spring

n. a safe or a tomb

Take It to Your Seat Centers—Reading & Language • EMC 2846 • © Evan-Moor Corp.

bear	sage
grave	loom
rare	reel
board	flounder
sole	root
toast	vault
refrain	cue
league	hamper

Homographs

Take It to Your Seat
Reading & Language Centers
EMC 2846 • © Evan-Moor Corp.

Homographs

Take It to Your Seat
Reading & Language Centers
EMC 2846 • © Evan-Moor Corp.

Homographs

Take It to Your Seat
Reading & Language Centers
EMC 2846 • © Evan-Moor Corp.

Homographs

Take It to Your Seat
Reading & Language Centers
EMC 2846 • © Evan-Moor Corp.

Homographs

Take It to Your Seat
Reading & Language Centers
EMC 2846 • © Evan-Moor Corp.

Homographs

Take It to Your Seat
Reading & Language Centers
EMC 2846 • © Evan-Moor Corp.

Homographs

Take It to Your Seat
Reading & Language Centers
EMC 2846 • © Evan-Moor Corp.

Homographs

Take It to Your Seat
Reading & Language Centers
EMC 2846 • © Evan-Moor Corp.

Homographs

Take It to Your Seat
Reading & Language Centers
EMC 2846 • © Evan-Moor Corp.

Homographs

Take It to Your Seat
Reading & Language Centers
EMC 2846 • © Evan-Moor Corp.

Homographs

Take It to Your Seat
Reading & Language Centers
EMC 2846 • © Evan-Moor Corp.

Homographs

Take It to Your Seat
Reading & Language Centers
EMC 2846 • © Evan-Moor Corp.

Homographs

Take It to Your Seat
Reading & Language Centers
EMC 2846 • © Evan-Moor Corp.

Homographs

Take It to Your Seat
Reading & Language Centers
EMC 2846 • © Evan-Moor Corp.

Homographs

Take It to Your Seat
Reading & Language Centers
EMC 2846 • © Evan-Moor Corp.

Homographs

Take It to Your Seat
Reading & Language Centers
EMC 2846 • © Evan-Moor Corp.

Greek and Latin Roots

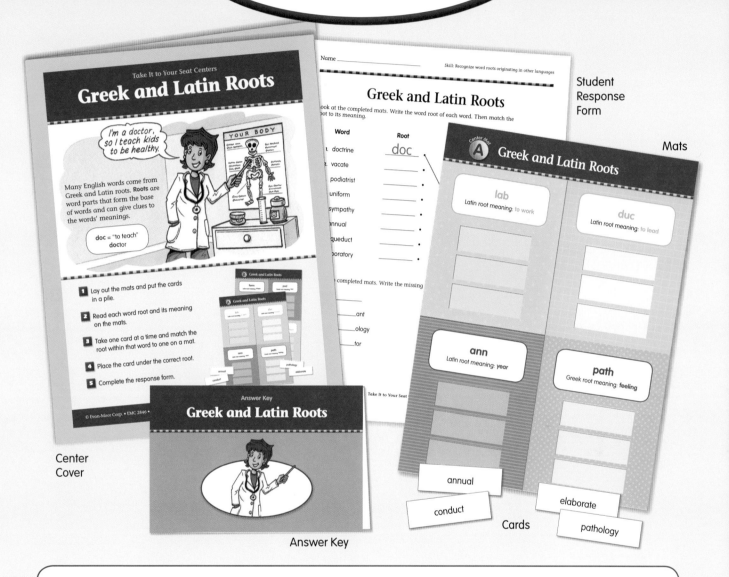

Center Cover

Answer Key

Student Response Form

Mats

Cards

Skill
Recognize word roots originating in other languages

Prepare the Center
Follow the directions on page 3.

Introduce the Center
Demonstrate how the center works. State the goal: *You will read each word card, find its root, and then place the card under the matching root on the mat.*

Greek and Latin Roots

Look at the completed mats. Write the word root of each word. Then match the root to its meaning.

Word	Root	Root's Meaning
1. doctrine	doc •	work
2. vacate	_____ •	lead
3. podiatrist	_____ •	year
4. uniform	_____ •	feeling
5. sympathy	_____ •	shape
6. annual	_____ •	foot
7. aqueduct	_____ •	empty
8. laboratory	_____ •	teach

Look at the completed mats. Write the missing word root to complete each word.

1. tri_____

2. _____ant

3. _____ology

4. _____tor

5. trans_____

6. _____trine

7. _____ual

8. _____or

Greek and Latin Roots

Many English words come from Greek and Latin roots. **Roots** are word parts that form the base of words and can give clues to the words' meanings.

doc = "to teach"
doctor

1 Lay out the mats and put the cards in a pile.

2 Read each word root and its meaning on the mats.

3 Take one card at a time and match the root within that word to one on a mat.

4 Place the card under the correct root.

5 Complete the response form.

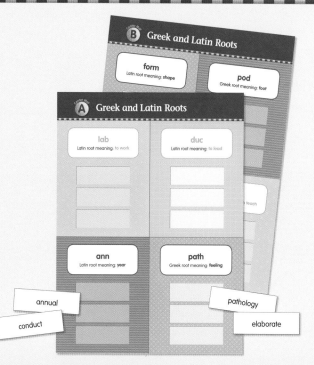

Greek and Latin Roots

Look at the completed mats. Write the word root of each word. Then match the root to its meaning.

Word	Root	Root's Meaning
1. doctrine	doc	work
2. vacate	vac	lead
3. podiatrist	pod	year
4. uniform	form	feeling
5. sympathy	path	shape
6. annual	ann	foot
7. aqueduct	duc	empty
8. laboratory	lab	teach

Look at the completed mats. Write the missing root to complete each word.

1. in**pod** | 5. trans**form**
2. **vac**ant | 6. **doc**trine
3. **path**ology | 7. **ann**ual
4. **doc**tor | 8. **lab**or

(fold)

Answer Key

Greek and Latin Roots

Answer Key

Greek and Latin Roots

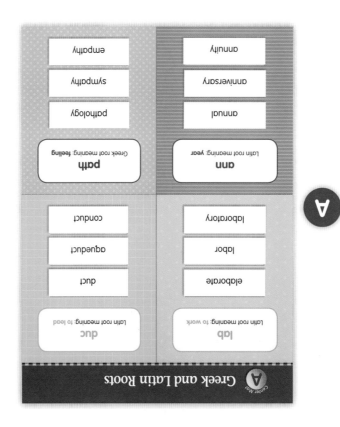

Center Mat **A** Greek and Latin Roots

ann Latin root meaning: **year**
- annual
- anniversary
- annuity

lab Latin root meaning: **to work**
- elaborate
- labor
- laboratory

path Greek root meaning: **feeling**
- pathology
- sympathy
- empathy

duc Latin root meaning: **to lead**
- duct
- aqueduct
- conduct

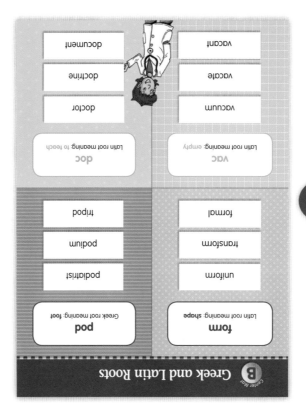

Center Mat **B** Greek and Latin Roots

form Latin root meaning: **shape**
- uniform
- transform
- formal

pod Greek root meaning: **foot**
- podiatrist
- podium
- tripod

vac Latin root meaning: **empty**
- vacuum
- vacate
- vacant

doc Latin root meaning: **to teach**
- doctor
- doctrine
- document

Greek and Latin Roots

lab
Latin root meaning: to work

duc
Latin root meaning: to lead

ann
Latin root meaning: **year**

path
Greek root meaning: **feeling**

B Greek and Latin Roots

form
Latin root meaning: **shape**

pod
Greek root meaning: **foot**

vac
Latin root meaning: empty

doc
Latin root meaning: to teach

Take It to Your Seat Centers—Reading & Language • EMC 2846 • © Evan-Moor Corp.

elaborate	annual
labor	anniversary
laboratory	annuity
duct	pathology
aqueduct	sympathy
conduct	empathy

Greek and Latin Roots

Take It to Your Seat Centers
Reading & Language
EMC 2846 • © Evan-Moor Corp.

Greek and Latin Roots

Take It to Your Seat Centers
Reading & Language
EMC 2846 • © Evan-Moor Corp.

Greek and Latin Roots

Take It to Your Seat Centers
Reading & Language
EMC 2846 • © Evan-Moor Corp.

Greek and Latin Roots

Take It to Your Seat Centers
Reading & Language
EMC 2846 • © Evan-Moor Corp.

Greek and Latin Roots

Take It to Your Seat Centers
Reading & Language
EMC 2846 • © Evan-Moor Corp.

Greek and Latin Roots

Take It to Your Seat Centers
Reading & Language
EMC 2846 • © Evan-Moor Corp.

Greek and Latin Roots

Take It to Your Seat Centers
Reading & Language
EMC 2846 • © Evan-Moor Corp.

Greek and Latin Roots

Take It to Your Seat Centers
Reading & Language
EMC 2846 • © Evan-Moor Corp.

Greek and Latin Roots

Take It to Your Seat Centers
Reading & Language
EMC 2846 • © Evan-Moor Corp.

Greek and Latin Roots

Take It to Your Seat Centers
Reading & Language
EMC 2846 • © Evan-Moor Corp.

Greek and Latin Roots

Take It to Your Seat Centers
Reading & Language
EMC 2846 • © Evan-Moor Corp.

Greek and Latin Roots

Take It to Your Seat Centers
Reading & Language
EMC 2846 • © Evan-Moor Corp.

uniform	vacuum
transform	vacate
formal	vacant
podiatrist	doctor
podium	doctrine
tripod	document

Greek and Latin Roots

Take It to Your Seat Centers
Reading & Language
EMC 2846 • © Evan-Moor Corp.

Greek and Latin Roots

Take It to Your Seat Centers
Reading & Language
EMC 2846 • © Evan-Moor Corp.

Greek and Latin Roots

Take It to Your Seat Centers
Reading & Language
EMC 2846 • © Evan-Moor Corp.

Greek and Latin Roots

Take It to Your Seat Centers
Reading & Language
EMC 2846 • © Evan-Moor Corp.

Greek and Latin Roots

Take It to Your Seat Centers
Reading & Language
EMC 2846 • © Evan-Moor Corp.

Greek and Latin Roots

Take It to Your Seat Centers
Reading & Language
EMC 2846 • © Evan-Moor Corp.

Greek and Latin Roots

Take It to Your Seat Centers
Reading & Language
EMC 2846 • © Evan-Moor Corp.

Greek and Latin Roots

Take It to Your Seat Centers
Reading & Language
EMC 2846 • © Evan-Moor Corp.

Greek and Latin Roots

Take It to Your Seat Centers
Reading & Language
EMC 2846 • © Evan-Moor Corp.

Greek and Latin Roots

Take It to Your Seat Centers
Reading & Language
EMC 2846 • © Evan-Moor Corp.

Greek and Latin Roots

Take It to Your Seat Centers
Reading & Language
EMC 2846 • © Evan-Moor Corp.

Greek and Latin Roots

Take It to Your Seat Centers
Reading & Language
EMC 2846 • © Evan-Moor Corp.

Prefixes

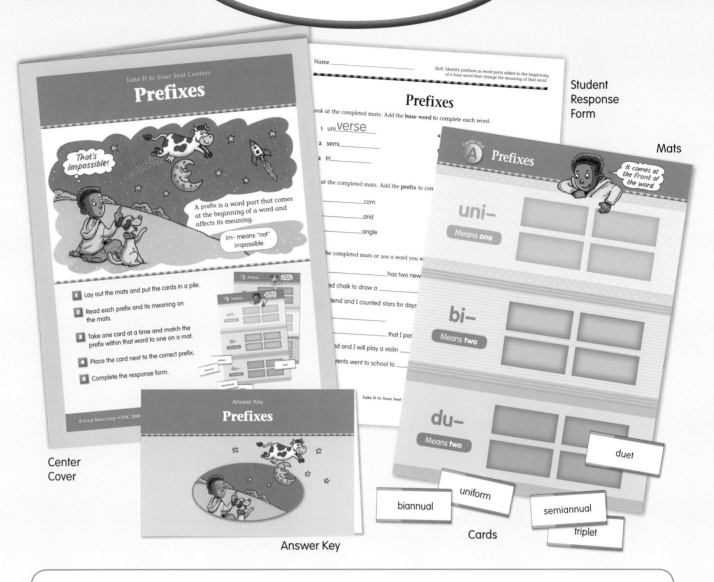

Center Cover

Answer Key

Student Response Form

Mats

Cards

Skill
Identify prefixes as word parts added to the beginning of a base word that change the meaning of that word

Prepare the Center
Follow the directions on page 3.

Introduce the Center
Demonstrate how the center works. State the goal: *You will read each word card, find its prefix, and then place the card next to the matching prefix on the mat.*

Prefixes

Look at the completed mats. Add the **base word** to complete each word.

1. uni**verse**_____

2. semi_____

3. tri_____

4. du_____

5. con_____

6. bi_____

Look at the completed mats. Add the **prefix** to complete each word.

1. _____corn

2. _____arid

3. _____angle

4. _____plex

5. _____fident

6. _____circle

Look at the completed mats or use a word you wrote above to complete each sentence.

1. My _____ has two new tires.

2. I used chalk to draw a _____ on the playground.

3. My friend and I counted stars for days: one million, one billion,

   one _____.

4. I am _____ that I passed the history test.

5. My friend and I will play a violin _____ in the talent show.

6. Jim's parents went to school to _____ with his math teacher.

Take It to Your Seat Centers—Reading & Language • EMC 2846 • © Evan-Moor Corp.

Prefixes

A **prefix** is a word part that comes at the beginning of a word and affects its meaning.

im- means "not"
impossible

1 Lay out the mats and put the cards in a pile.

2 Read each prefix and its meaning on the mats.

3 Take one card at a time and match the prefix within that word to one on a mat.

4 Place the card next to the correct prefix.

5 Complete the response form.

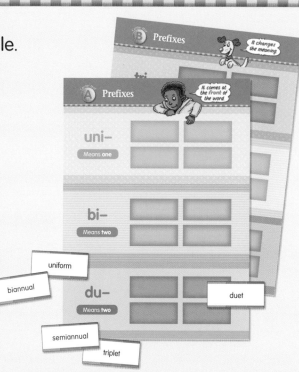

Prefixes

Possible answers are given.

Look at the completed mats. Add the **base word** to complete each word.

1. uni_verse
2. semi_annual
3. tri_cycle
4. du_et
5. con_fident
6. bi_noculars

Look at the completed mats. Add the **prefix** to complete each word.

1. uni_corn
2. semi_arid
3. tri_angle
4. du_plex
5. con_fident
6. semi_circle

Look at the completed mats or use a word you wrote above to complete each sentence.

1. My **bicycle** has two new tires.
2. I used chalk to draw a **semicircle** on the playground.
3. My friend and I counted stars for days: one million, one billion, one **trillion**.
4. I am **confident** that I passed the history test.
5. My friend and I will play a violin **duet** in the talent show.
6. Jim's parents went to school to **confer** with his math teacher.

Response Form

(fold)

Answer Key

Prefixes

Answer Key
Prefixes

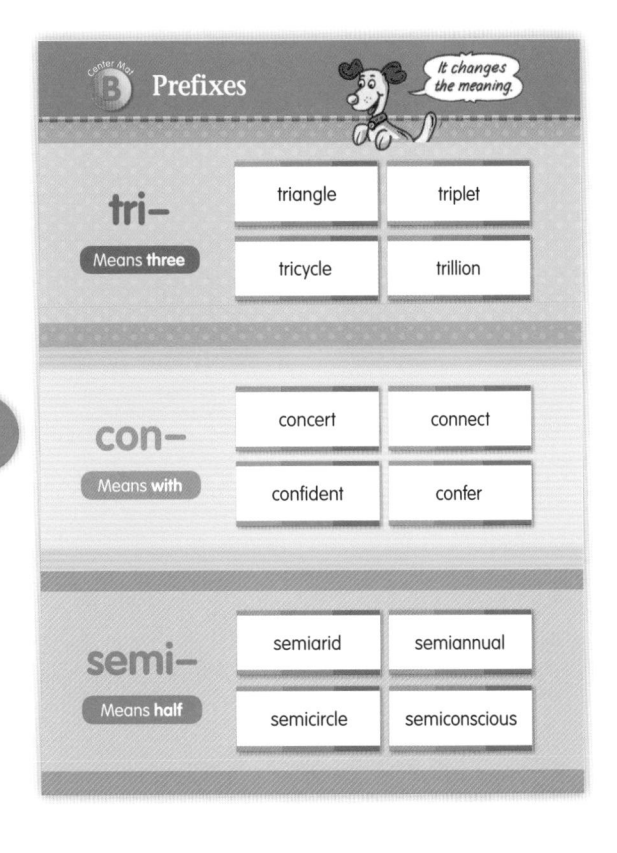

A Prefixes
It comes at the front of the word.

uni–
Means **one**

unicycle	universe
unicorn	uniform

bi–
Means **two**

bicycle	biannual
billion	binoculars

du–
Means **two**

duplicate	duet
duplex	dual

B Prefixes
It changes the meaning.

tri–
Means **three**

triangle	triplet
tricycle	trillion

con–
Means **with**

concert	connect
confident	confer

semi–
Means **half**

semiarid	semiannual
semicircle	semiconscious

It comes at the ***front*** of the word.

uni–

Means **one**

bi–

Means **two**

du–

Means **two**

It changes the meaning.

tri–

Means **three**

con–

Means **with**

semi–

Means **half**

unicycle	universe	unicorn
uniform	bicycle	biannual
billion	binoculars	triangle
tricycle	trillion	triplet
duplicate	duet	duplex
dual	concert	connect
confer	confident	semicircle
semiarid	semiannual	semiconscious

Prefixes

Take It to Your Seat Centers
Reading & Language
EMC 2846 • © Evan-Moor Corp.

Prefixes

Take It to Your Seat Centers
Reading & Language
EMC 2846 • © Evan-Moor Corp.

Prefixes

Take It to Your Seat Centers
Reading & Language
EMC 2846 • © Evan-Moor Corp.

Prefixes

Take It to Your Seat Centers
Reading & Language
EMC 2846 • © Evan-Moor Corp.

Prefixes

Take It to Your Seat Centers
Reading & Language
EMC 2846 • © Evan-Moor Corp.

Prefixes

Take It to Your Seat Centers
Reading & Language
EMC 2846 • © Evan-Moor Corp.

Prefixes

Take It to Your Seat Centers
Reading & Language
EMC 2846 • © Evan-Moor Corp.

Prefixes

Take It to Your Seat Centers
Reading & Language
EMC 2846 • © Evan-Moor Corp.

Prefixes

Take It to Your Seat Centers
Reading & Language
EMC 2846 • © Evan-Moor Corp.

Prefixes

Take It to Your Seat Centers
Reading & Language
EMC 2846 • © Evan-Moor Corp.

Prefixes

Take It to Your Seat Centers
Reading & Language
EMC 2846 • © Evan-Moor Corp.

Prefixes

Take It to Your Seat Centers
Reading & Language
EMC 2846 • © Evan-Moor Corp.

Prefixes

Take It to Your Seat Centers
Reading & Language
EMC 2846 • © Evan-Moor Corp.

Prefixes

Take It to Your Seat Centers
Reading & Language
EMC 2846 • © Evan-Moor Corp.

Prefixes

Take It to Your Seat Centers
Reading & Language
EMC 2846 • © Evan-Moor Corp.

Prefixes

Take It to Your Seat Centers
Reading & Language
EMC 2846 • © Evan-Moor Corp.

Prefixes

Take It to Your Seat Centers
Reading & Language
EMC 2846 • © Evan-Moor Corp.

Prefixes

Take It to Your Seat Centers
Reading & Language
EMC 2846 • © Evan-Moor Corp.

Prefixes

Take It to Your Seat Centers
Reading & Language
EMC 2846 • © Evan-Moor Corp.

Prefixes

Take It to Your Seat Centers
Reading & Language
EMC 2846 • © Evan-Moor Corp.

Prefixes

Take It to Your Seat Centers
Reading & Language
EMC 2846 • © Evan-Moor Corp.

Prefixes

Take It to Your Seat Centers
Reading & Language
EMC 2846 • © Evan-Moor Corp.

Prefixes

Take It to Your Seat Centers
Reading & Language
EMC 2846 • © Evan-Moor Corp.

Prefixes

Take It to Your Seat Centers
Reading & Language
EMC 2846 • © Evan-Moor Corp.

Suffixes

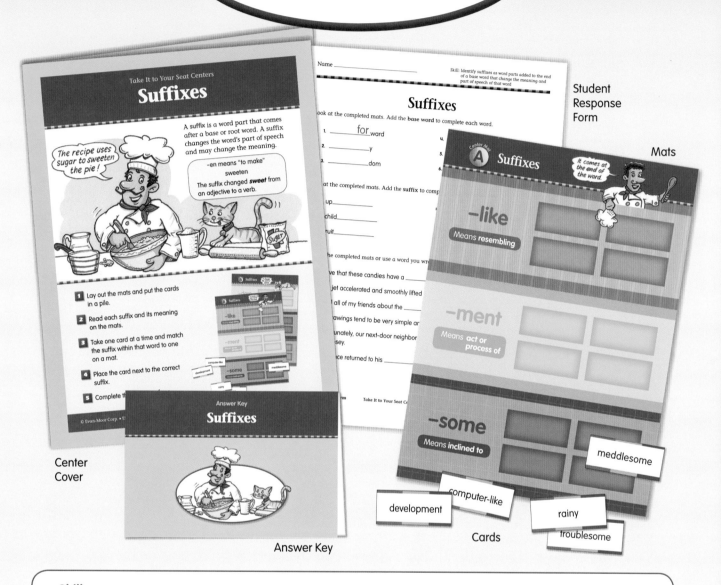

Center Cover

Answer Key

Student Response Form

Mats

Cards

Skill
Identify suffixes as word parts added to the end of a base word that change the meaning and part of speech of that word

Prepare the Center
Follow the directions on page 3.

Introduce the Center
Demonstrate how the center works. State the goal: *You will read each word card, find its suffix, and then place the card next to the matching suffix on the mat.*

Suffixes

Look at the completed mats. Add the **base word** to complete each word.

1. _____for___ward

2. _____y

3. _____dom

4. _____like

5. _____some

6. _____ment

Look at the completed mats. Add the **suffix** to complete each word.

1. up_____

2. child_____

3. fruit_____

4. develop_____

5. tire_____

6. free_____

Look at the completed mats or use a word you wrote above to complete each sentence.

1. I love that these candies have a _____ flavor.

2. The jet accelerated and smoothly lifted _____ at takeoff.

3. I told all of my friends about the _____ movie we saw last night.

4. My drawings tend to be very simple and _____.

5. Unfortunately, our next-door neighbor, Mrs. Cherry, is _____ and nosey.

6. The prince returned to his _____ after traveling around the world.

Suffixes

The recipe uses sugar to sweeten the pie!

A **suffix** is a word part that comes after a base or root word. A suffix changes the word's part of speech and may change the meaning.

> **-en** means "to make"
>
> sweet**en**
>
> The suffix changed **sweet** from an adjective to a verb.

1 Lay out the mats and put the cards in a pile.

2 Read each suffix and its meaning on the mats.

3 Take one card at a time and match the suffix within that word to one on a mat.

4 Place the card next to the correct suffix.

5 Complete the response form.

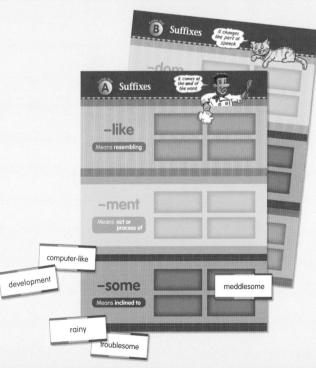

74

Response Form

Suffixes — Possible answers are given.

Look at the completed mats. Add the **base word** to complete each word.

1. for**ward**
2. sunn**y**
3. bore**dom**
4. **life**like
5. **awe**some
6. experi**ment**

Look at the completed mats. Add the **suffix** to complete each word.

1. up**ward**
2. child**like**
3. fruit**y**
4. develop**ment**
5. tire**some**
6. free**dom**

Look at the completed mats or use a word you wrote above to complete each sentence.

1. I love that these candies have a **fruity** flavor.
2. The jet accelerated and smoothly lifted **upward** at takeoff.
3. I told all of my friends about the **funny** movie we saw last night.
4. My drawings tend to be very simple and **childlike**.
5. Unfortunately, our next-door neighbor, Mrs. Cherry, is **meddlesome** and nosey.
6. The prince returned to his **kingdom** after traveling around the world.

Answer Key

Suffixes

Answer Key
Suffixes

A Suffixes

It comes at the end of the word.

-like
Means **resembling**

| childlike | lifelike |
| homelike | computer-like |

-ment
Means **act or process of**

| government | development |
| experiment | amusement |

-some
Means **inclined to**

| awesome | troublesome |
| tiresome | meddlesome |

B Suffixes

It changes the part of speech.

-dom
Means **state of being**

| freedom | boredom |
| wisdom | kingdom |

-ward
Means **direction**

| forward | backward |
| onward | upward |

-y
Means **being or having**

| fruity | rainy |
| chewy | sunny |

It comes at the **end** of the word.

–like

Means **resembling**

–ment

Means **act or process of**

–some

Means **inclined to**

Take It to Your Seat Centers—Reading & Language • EMC 2846 • © Evan-Moor Corp.

It changes the part of speech.

–dom

Means **state of being**

–ward

Means **direction**

–y

Means **being or having**

childlike	lifelike	homelike
computer-like	government	development
experiment	amusement	awesome
tiresome	meddlesome	troublesome
freedom	boredom	wisdom
kingdom	forward	backward
upward	onward	fruity
chewy	rainy	sunny

Suffixes	Suffixes	Suffixes
Take It to Your Seat Centers Reading & Language EMC 2846 • © Evan-Moor Corp.	Take It to Your Seat Centers Reading & Language EMC 2846 • © Evan-Moor Corp.	Take It to Your Seat Centers Reading & Language EMC 2846 • © Evan-Moor Corp.
Suffixes	Suffixes	Suffixes
Take It to Your Seat Centers Reading & Language EMC 2846 • © Evan-Moor Corp.	Take It to Your Seat Centers Reading & Language EMC 2846 • © Evan-Moor Corp.	Take It to Your Seat Centers Reading & Language EMC 2846 • © Evan-Moor Corp.
Suffixes	Suffixes	Suffixes
Take It to Your Seat Centers Reading & Language EMC 2846 • © Evan-Moor Corp.	Take It to Your Seat Centers Reading & Language EMC 2846 • © Evan-Moor Corp.	Take It to Your Seat Centers Reading & Language EMC 2846 • © Evan-Moor Corp.
Suffixes	Suffixes	Suffixes
Take It to Your Seat Centers Reading & Language EMC 2846 • © Evan-Moor Corp.	Take It to Your Seat Centers Reading & Language EMC 2846 • © Evan-Moor Corp.	Take It to Your Seat Centers Reading & Language EMC 2846 • © Evan-Moor Corp.
Suffixes	Suffixes	Suffixes
Take It to Your Seat Centers Reading & Language EMC 2846 • © Evan-Moor Corp.	Take It to Your Seat Centers Reading & Language EMC 2846 • © Evan-Moor Corp.	Take It to Your Seat Centers Reading & Language EMC 2846 • © Evan-Moor Corp.
Suffixes	Suffixes	Suffixes
Take It to Your Seat Centers Reading & Language EMC 2846 • © Evan-Moor Corp.	Take It to Your Seat Centers Reading & Language EMC 2846 • © Evan-Moor Corp.	Take It to Your Seat Centers Reading & Language EMC 2846 • © Evan-Moor Corp.
Suffixes	Suffixes	Suffixes
Take It to Your Seat Centers Reading & Language EMC 2846 • © Evan-Moor Corp.	Take It to Your Seat Centers Reading & Language EMC 2846 • © Evan-Moor Corp.	Take It to Your Seat Centers Reading & Language EMC 2846 • © Evan-Moor Corp.
Suffixes	Suffixes	Suffixes
Take It to Your Seat Centers Reading & Language EMC 2846 • © Evan-Moor Corp.	Take It to Your Seat Centers Reading & Language EMC 2846 • © Evan-Moor Corp.	Take It to Your Seat Centers Reading & Language EMC 2846 • © Evan-Moor Corp.

Analogies

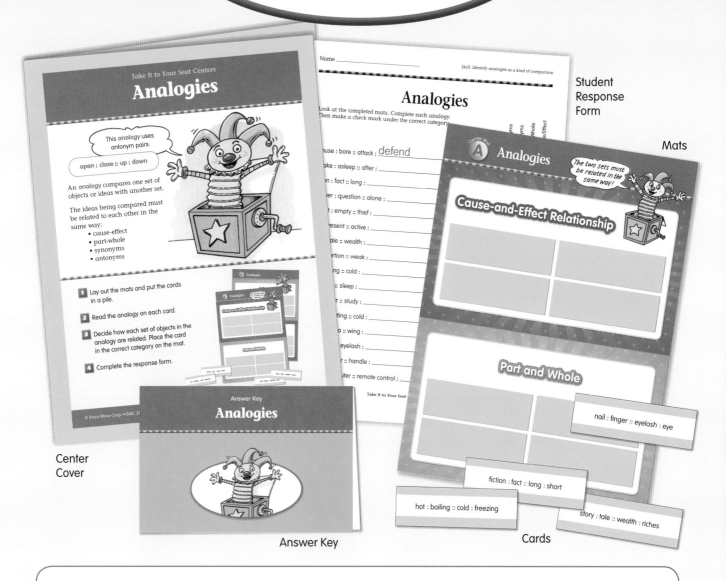

Center Cover

Answer Key

Cards

Mats

Student Response Form

Skill
Identify analogies as a kind of comparison

Prepare the Center
Follow the directions on page 3.

Introduce the Center
Demonstrate how the center works. State the goal:
You will read each analogy card, decide how the two sets of words are related, and then place the card in the correct category on the mat.

Analogies

Look at the completed mats. Complete each analogy.
Then make a check mark under the correct category.

	Synonyms	Antonyms	Part/Whole	Cause/Effect
amuse : bore :: attack : _defend_ _____		✓		
awake : asleep :: after : _____				
fiction : fact :: long : _____				
answer : question :: alone : _____				
vacant : empty :: thief : _____				
gift : present :: active : _____				
story : tale :: wealth : _____				
part : portion :: weak : _____				
hot : boiling :: cold : _____				
run : tired :: sleep : _____				
listen : hear :: study : _____				
heat : sweating :: cold : _____				
lens : camera :: wing : _____				
nail : finger :: eyelash : _____				
staple : stapler :: handle : _____				
mouse : computer :: remote control : _____				

Analogies

> This **analogy** uses antonym pairs.

> open : close :: up : down

An **analogy** compares one set of objects or ideas with another set.

The ideas being compared must be related to each other in the same way:

- cause-effect
- part-whole
- synonyms
- antonyms

1. Lay out the mats and put the cards in a pile.

2. Read the analogy on each card.

3. Decide how each set of objects in the analogy are related. Place the card in the correct category on the mat.

4. Complete the response form.

Analogies

Answer Key

(fold)

Response Form

Analogies

Look at the completed mats. Complete each analogy.
Then make a check mark under the correct category.

	Synonyms	Antonyms	Part/Whole	Cause/Effect
amuse : bore :: attack : **defend**		✓		
awake : asleep :: after : **before**		✓		
fiction : fact :: long : **short**		✓		
answer : question :: alone : **together**		✓		
vacant : empty :: thief : **robber**	✓			
gift : present :: active : **lively**	✓			
story : tale :: wealth : **riches**	✓			
part : portion :: weak : **feeble**	✓			
hot : boiling :: cold : **freezing**				✓
run : tired :: sleep : **rested**				✓
listen : hear :: study : **learn**				✓
heat : sweating :: cold : **shivering**				✓
lens : camera :: wing : **plane**			✓	
nail : finger :: eyelash : **eye**			✓	
staple : stapler :: handle : **door**			✓	
mouse : computer :: remote control : **TV**			✓	

Answer Key

Analogies

Analogies

The two sets must be related in the same way!

Cause-and-Effect Relationship

hot : boiling :: cold : freezing	run : tired :: sleep : rested
listen : hear :: study : learn	heat : sweating :: cold : shivering

Part and Whole

lens : camera :: wing : plane	nail : finger :: eyelash : eye
mouse : computer :: remote control : TV	staple : stapler :: handle : door

Analogies

Antonyms

amuse : bore :: attack : defend	awake : asleep :: after : before
fiction : fact :: long : short	answer : question :: alone : together

Synonyms

vacant : empty :: thief : robber	gift : present :: active : lively
part : portion :: weak : feeble	story : tale :: wealth : riches

 Analogies

The two sets must be related in the same way!

Cause-and-Effect Relationship

Part and Whole

Analogies

Antonyms

Synonyms

amuse : bore :: attack : defend	awake : asleep :: after : before
fiction : fact :: long : short	answer : question :: alone : together
vacant : empty :: thief : robber	gift : present :: active : lively
story : tale :: wealth : riches	part : portion :: weak : feeble
hot : boiling :: cold : freezing	run : tired :: sleep : rested
listen : hear :: study : learn	heat : sweating :: cold : shivering
lens : camera :: wing : plane	nail : finger :: eyelash : eye
staple : stapler :: handle : door	mouse : computer :: remote control : TV

Analogies

Take It to Your Seat Centers
Reading & Language
EMC 2846 • © Evan-Moor Corp.

Analogies

Take It to Your Seat Centers
Reading & Language
EMC 2846 • © Evan-Moor Corp.

Analogies

Take It to Your Seat Centers
Reading & Language
EMC 2846 • © Evan-Moor Corp.

Analogies

Take It to Your Seat Centers
Reading & Language
EMC 2846 • © Evan-Moor Corp.

Analogies

Take It to Your Seat Centers
Reading & Language
EMC 2846 • © Evan-Moor Corp.

Analogies

Take It to Your Seat Centers
Reading & Language
EMC 2846 • © Evan-Moor Corp.

Analogies

Take It to Your Seat Centers
Reading & Language
EMC 2846 • © Evan-Moor Corp.

Analogies

Take It to Your Seat Centers
Reading & Language
EMC 2846 • © Evan-Moor Corp.

Analogies

Take It to Your Seat Centers
Reading & Language
EMC 2846 • © Evan-Moor Corp.

Analogies

Take It to Your Seat Centers
Reading & Language
EMC 2846 • © Evan-Moor Corp.

Analogies

Take It to Your Seat Centers
Reading & Language
EMC 2846 • © Evan-Moor Corp.

Analogies

Take It to Your Seat Centers
Reading & Language
EMC 2846 • © Evan-Moor Corp.

Analogies

Take It to Your Seat Centers
Reading & Language
EMC 2846 • © Evan-Moor Corp.

Analogies

Take It to Your Seat Centers
Reading & Language
EMC 2846 • © Evan-Moor Corp.

Analogies

Take It to Your Seat Centers
Reading & Language
EMC 2846 • © Evan-Moor Corp.

Analogies

Take It to Your Seat Centers
Reading & Language
EMC 2846 • © Evan-Moor Corp.

Idioms

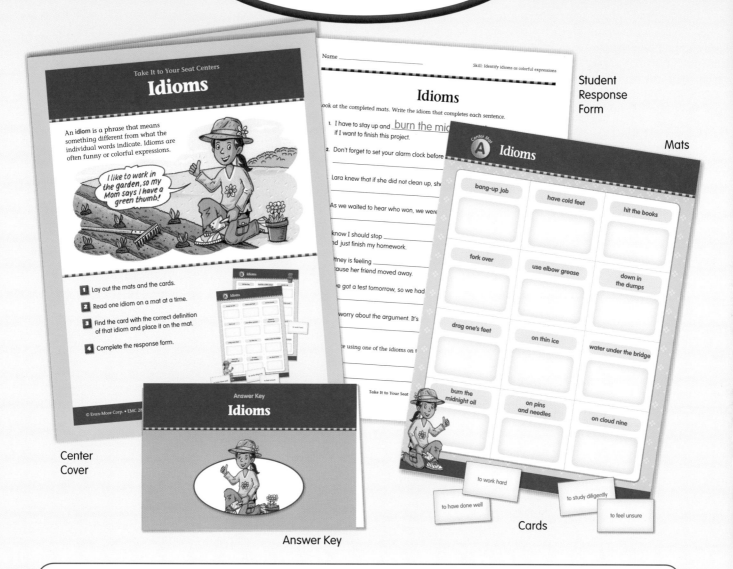

Center Cover

Student Response Form

Answer Key

Mats

Cards

Skill
Identify idioms as colorful expressions

Prepare the Center
Follow the directions on page 3.

Introduce the Center
Demonstrate how the center works. State the goal:
You will read each idiom on the mats and place the correct definition card below it.

Idioms

Look at the completed mats. Write the idiom that completes each sentence.

1. I have to stay up and _burn the midnight oil_____ if I want to finish this project.

2. Don't forget to set your alarm clock before you

   _____.

3. Lara knew that if she did not clean up, she'd be

   _____ with Mom.

4. As we waited to hear who won, we were

   _____.

5. I know I should stop _____ and just finish my homework.

6. Brittney is feeling _____ because her friend moved away.

7. We've got a test tomorrow, so we had better

   _____.

8. Don't worry about the argument. It's

   _____.

Write a sentence using one of the idioms on the mats. Then underline the idiom.

_____

_____

Idioms

An **idiom** is a phrase that means something different from what the individual words indicate. Idioms are often funny or colorful expressions.

> I like to work in the garden, so my Mom says I have a green thumb!

1 Lay out the mats and the cards.

2 Read one idiom on a mat at a time.

3 Find the card with the correct definition of that idiom and place it on the mat.

4 Complete the response form.

98

Idioms

Answer Key

(fold)

Response Form

Idioms Possible answers are given.

Look at the completed mats. Write the idiom that completes each sentence.

1. I have to stay up and <u>burn the midnight oil</u>
if I want to finish this project.

2. Don't forget to set your alarm clock before you
<u>hit the hay</u>.

3. Lara knew that if she did not clean up, she'd be
<u>on thin ice</u> with Mom.

4. As we waited to hear who won, we were
<u>on pins and needles</u>.

5. I know I should stop <u>dragging my feet</u>
and just finish my homework.

6. Brittney is feeling <u>down in the dumps</u>
because her friend moved away.

7. We've got a test tomorrow, so we had better
<u>hit the books</u>.

8. Don't worry about the argument. It's
<u>water under the bridge</u>.

Write a sentence using one of the idioms on the mats. Then underline the idiom.

<u>Answers will vary.</u>

_____

Answer Key

Idioms

A — Idioms

bang-up job	have cold feet	hit the books
to have done well	to feel unsure	to study diligently
fork over	**use elbow grease**	**down in the dumps**
to hand over	to work hard	to be depressed
drag one's feet	**on thin ice**	**water under the bridge**
to delay a decision	to be in a difficult situation	something that happened in the past; over and done with
burn the midnight oil	**on pins and needles**	**on cloud nine**
to stay up late	to wait nervously	to feel very happy

B — Idioms

hit the hay	feel like a fifth wheel	butter up
to go to bed	to feel unwanted, out of place	to compliment someone
get up on the wrong side of the bed	**shoot the breeze**	**hugged the road**
to be grumpy	to sit around and visit with a friend	drove easily and safely
steal the spotlight	**bite your tongue**	**isn't my cup of tea**
to stand out above others	don't say what you are thinking	not a subject or topic I'm interested in
call it a day	**know the ropes**	**off the top of my head**
to quit a task for the time being	to be experienced at a task	a quickly developed thought

Idioms

bang-up job	have cold feet	hit the books
fork over	use elbow grease	down in the dumps
drag one's feet	on thin ice	water under the bridge
burn the midnight oil	on pins and needles	on cloud nine

Take It to Your Seat Centers—Reading & Language • EMC 2846 • © Evan-Moor Corp.

B Idioms

hit the hay

feel like a fifth wheel

butter up

get up on the wrong side of the bed

shoot the breeze

hugged the road

steal the spotlight

bite your tongue

isn't my cup of tea

call it a day

know the ropes

off the top of my head

Take It to Your Seat Centers—Reading & Language • EMC 2846 • © Evan-Moor Corp.

to have done well	to feel unsure	to study diligently
to feel unwanted, out of place	to hand over	to work hard
to be depressed	to delay a decision	to be in a difficult situation
to go to bed	something that happened in the past; over and done with	to stay up late
to wait nervously	to compliment someone	to feel very happy
to be grumpy	to sit around and visit with a friend	drove easily and safely
to be experienced at a task	a quickly developed thought	to stand out above others
not a subject or topic I'm interested in	to quit a task for the time being	don't say what you are thinking

Idioms

Take It to Your Seat Centers
Reading & Language
EMC 2846 • © Evan-Moor Corp.

Idioms

Take It to Your Seat Centers
Reading & Language
EMC 2846 • © Evan-Moor Corp.

Idioms

Take It to Your Seat Centers
Reading & Language
EMC 2846 • © Evan-Moor Corp.

Idioms

Take It to Your Seat Centers
Reading & Language
EMC 2846 • © Evan-Moor Corp.

Idioms

Take It to Your Seat Centers
Reading & Language
EMC 2846 • © Evan-Moor Corp.

Idioms

Take It to Your Seat Centers
Reading & Language
EMC 2846 • © Evan-Moor Corp.

Idioms

Take It to Your Seat Centers
Reading & Language
EMC 2846 • © Evan-Moor Corp.

Idioms

Take It to Your Seat Centers
Reading & Language
EMC 2846 • © Evan-Moor Corp.

Idioms

Take It to Your Seat Centers
Reading & Language
EMC 2846 • © Evan-Moor Corp.

Idioms

Take It to Your Seat Centers
Reading & Language
EMC 2846 • © Evan-Moor Corp.

Idioms

Take It to Your Seat Centers
Reading & Language
EMC 2846 • © Evan-Moor Corp.

Idioms

Take It to Your Seat Centers
Reading & Language
EMC 2846 • © Evan-Moor Corp.

Idioms

Take It to Your Seat Centers
Reading & Language
EMC 2846 • © Evan-Moor Corp.

Idioms

Take It to Your Seat Centers
Reading & Language
EMC 2846 • © Evan-Moor Corp.

Idioms

Take It to Your Seat Centers
Reading & Language
EMC 2846 • © Evan-Moor Corp.

Idioms

Take It to Your Seat Centers
Reading & Language
EMC 2846 • © Evan-Moor Corp.

Idioms

Take It to Your Seat Centers
Reading & Language
EMC 2846 • © Evan-Moor Corp.

Idioms

Take It to Your Seat Centers
Reading & Language
EMC 2846 • © Evan-Moor Corp.

Idioms

Take It to Your Seat Centers
Reading & Language
EMC 2846 • © Evan-Moor Corp.

Idioms

Take It to Your Seat Centers
Reading & Language
EMC 2846 • © Evan-Moor Corp.

Idioms

Take It to Your Seat Centers
Reading & Language
EMC 2846 • © Evan-Moor Corp.

Idioms

Take It to Your Seat Centers
Reading & Language
EMC 2846 • © Evan-Moor Corp.

Idioms

Take It to Your Seat Centers
Reading & Language
EMC 2846 • © Evan-Moor Corp.

Idioms

Take It to Your Seat Centers
Reading & Language
EMC 2846 • © Evan-Moor Corp.

Similes & Metaphors

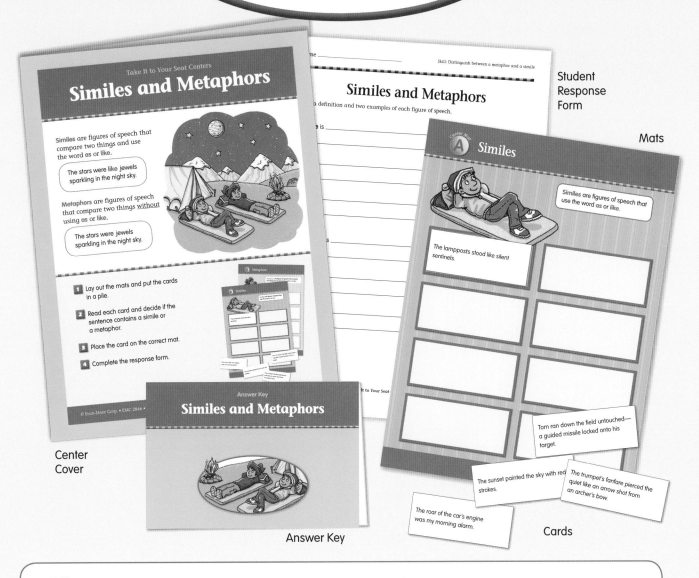

Center Cover

Answer Key

Student Response Form

Mats

Cards

Skill
Distinguish between a metaphor and a simile

Prepare the Center
Follow the directions on page 3.

Introduce the Center
Demonstrate how the center works. State the goal: *You will read each sentence card and decide if it contains a simile or a metaphor, then place the card on the correct mat.*

Similes and Metaphors

Write a definition and two examples of each figure of speech.

A **simile** is _____

_____

1. _____

_____

2. _____

_____

A **metaphor** is _____

_____

1. _____

_____

2. _____

_____

Similes and Metaphors

Similes are figures of speech that compare two things and use the word **as** or **like**.

> The stars were **like** jewels sparkling in the night sky.

Metaphors are figures of speech that compare two things <u>without</u> using **as** or **like**.

> The stars were jewels sparkling in the night sky.

1 Lay out the mats and put the cards in a pile.

2 Read each card and decide if the sentence contains a simile or a metaphor.

3 Place the card on the correct mat.

4 Complete the response form.

Similes and Metaphors

Write a definition and two examples of each figure of speech.

A **simile** is a figure of speech that compares two things and uses the word *as* or *like*.

_____

1. _____

Answers will vary.

2. _____

_____

A **metaphor** is a figure of speech that compares two things without using the word *as* or *like*.

_____

1. _____

Answers will vary.

2. _____

_____

Response Form

(fold)

Answer Key

Similes and Metaphors

Answer Key
Similes and Metaphors

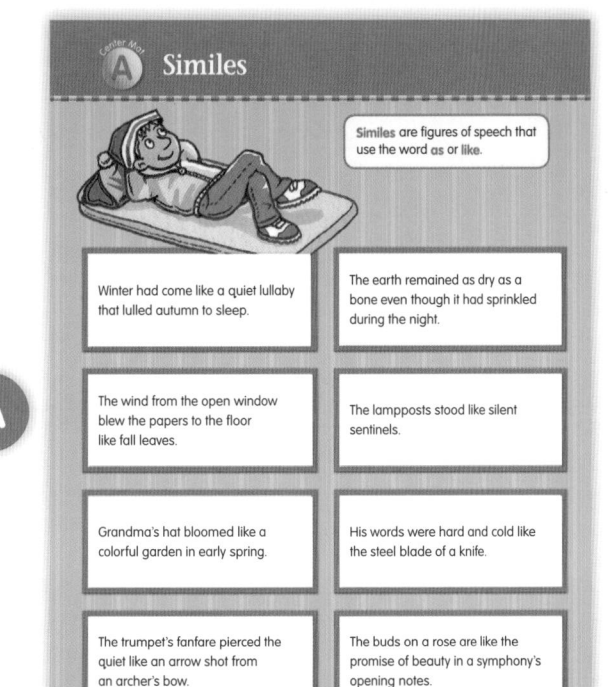

Similes

Similes are figures of speech that use the word **as** or **like**.

Winter had come like a quiet lullaby that lulled autumn to sleep.

The earth remained as dry as a bone even though it had sprinkled during the night.

The wind from the open window blew the papers to the floor like fall leaves.

The lampposts stood like silent sentinels.

Grandma's hat bloomed like a colorful garden in early spring.

His words were hard and cold like the steel blade of a knife.

The trumpet's fanfare pierced the quiet like an arrow shot from an archer's bow.

The buds on a rose are like the promise of beauty in a symphony's opening notes.

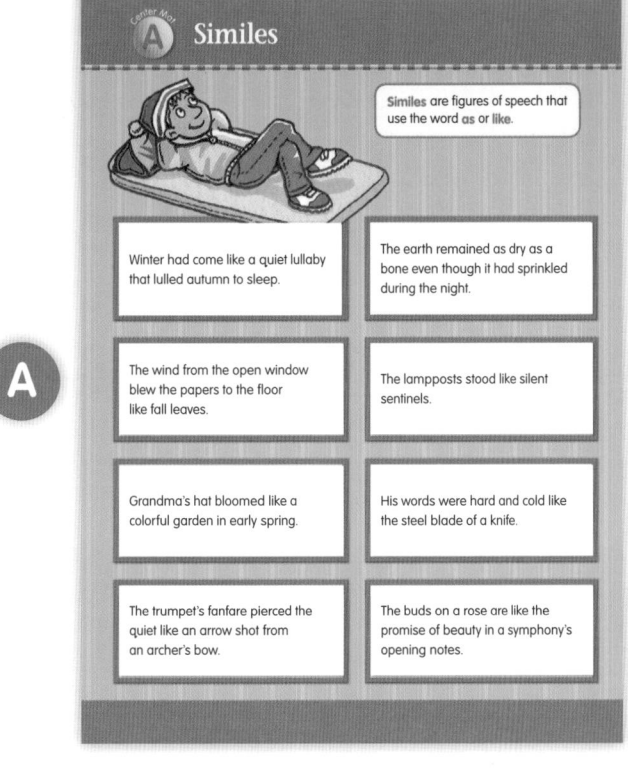

Metaphors

Metaphors are figures of speech that compare two things but do <u>not</u> use the word **as** or **like**.

Tom ran down the field untouched—a guided missile locked onto his target.

The runner was a thoroughbred, clearing the hurdles with ease.

The scarecrow stood alone—a former friend forgotten in the hustle of spring planting.

The roar of the car's engine was my morning alarm.

The green grass was a soft carpet for my bare toes.

The fog was a blanket of gray covering the town.

The sunset painted the sky with red strokes.

My brother's stomach is a bottomless pit.

Similes

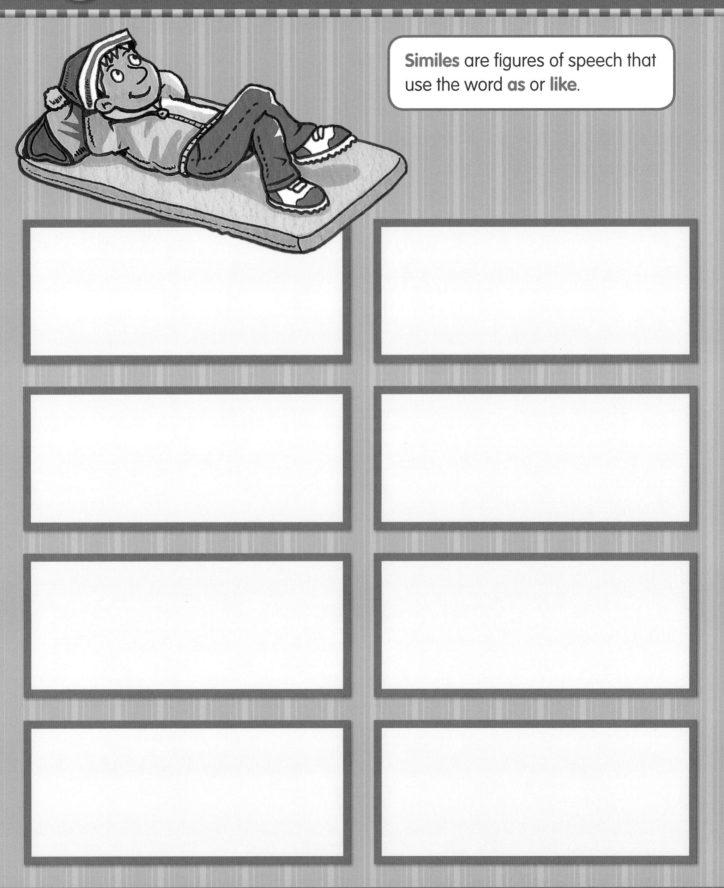

Similes are figures of speech that use the word **as** or **like**.

Metaphors

Metaphors are figures of speech that compare two things but do <u>not</u> use the word **as** or **like**.

Take It to Your Seat Centers—Reading & Language • EMC 2846 • © Evan-Moor Corp.

Winter had come like a quiet lullaby that lulled autumn to sleep.

The earth remained as dry as a bone even though it had sprinkled during the night.

The wind from the open window blew the papers to the floor like fall leaves.

The lampposts stood like silent sentinels.

Grandma's hat bloomed like a colorful garden in early spring.

His words were hard and cold like the steel blade of a knife.

The trumpet's fanfare pierced the quiet like an arrow shot from an archer's bow.

The buds on a rose are like the promise of beauty in a symphony's opening notes.

Similes and Metaphors

Take It to Your Seat Centers
Reading & Language
EMC 2846 • © Evan-Moor Corp.

Similes and Metaphors

Take It to Your Seat Centers
Reading & Language
EMC 2846 • © Evan-Moor Corp.

Similes and Metaphors

Take It to Your Seat Centers
Reading & Language
EMC 2846 • © Evan-Moor Corp.

Similes and Metaphors

Take It to Your Seat Centers
Reading & Language
EMC 2846 • © Evan-Moor Corp.

Similes and Metaphors

Take It to Your Seat Centers
Reading & Language
EMC 2846 • © Evan-Moor Corp.

Similes and Metaphors

Take It to Your Seat Centers
Reading & Language
EMC 2846 • © Evan-Moor Corp.

Similes and Metaphors

Take It to Your Seat Centers
Reading & Language
EMC 2846 • © Evan-Moor Corp.

Similes and Metaphors

Take It to Your Seat Centers
Reading & Language
EMC 2846 • © Evan-Moor Corp.

Tom ran down the field untouched—a guided missile locked onto his target.

The runner was a thoroughbred, clearing the hurdles with ease.

The scarecrow stood alone—a former friend forgotten in the hustle of spring planting.

The roar of the car's engine was my morning alarm.

The green grass was a soft carpet for my bare toes.

The fog was a blanket of gray covering the town.

The sunset painted the sky with red strokes.

My brother's stomach is a bottomless pit.

Similes and Metaphors

Take It to Your Seat Centers
Reading & Language
EMC 2846 • © Evan-Moor Corp.

Similes and Metaphors

Take It to Your Seat Centers
Reading & Language
EMC 2846 • © Evan-Moor Corp.

Similes and Metaphors

Take It to Your Seat Centers
Reading & Language
EMC 2846 • © Evan-Moor Corp.

Similes and Metaphors

Take It to Your Seat Centers
Reading & Language
EMC 2846 • © Evan-Moor Corp.

Similes and Metaphors

Take It to Your Seat Centers
Reading & Language
EMC 2846 • © Evan-Moor Corp.

Similes and Metaphors

Take It to Your Seat Centers
Reading & Language
EMC 2846 • © Evan-Moor Corp.

Similes and Metaphors

Take It to Your Seat Centers
Reading & Language
EMC 2846 • © Evan-Moor Corp.

Similes and Metaphors

Take It to Your Seat Centers
Reading & Language
EMC 2846 • © Evan-Moor Corp.

Using Context Clues

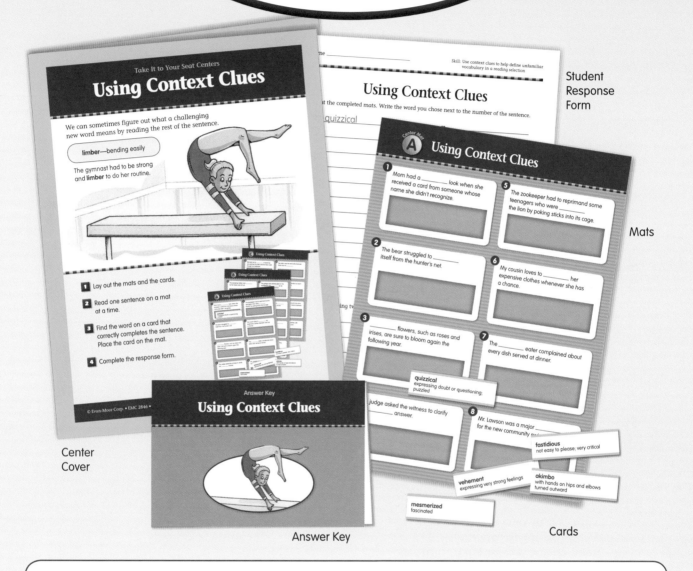

Student Response Form

Mats

Cards

Center Cover

Answer Key

Skill
Use context clues to help define unfamiliar vocabulary in a reading selection

Prepare the Center
Follow the directions on page 3.

Introduce the Center
Demonstrate how the center works. State the goal:
You will read each sentence on the mats and place the card that correctly completes the sentence on the mat.

Using Context Clues

Look at the completed mats. Write the word you chose next to the number of the sentence.

1. quizzical _____

2. _____

3. _____

4. _____

5. _____

6. _____

7. _____

8. _____

9. _____

10. _____

11. _____

12. _____

13. _____

14. _____

15. _____

16. _____

17. _____

18. _____

19. _____

20. _____

21. _____

22. _____

23. _____

24. _____

Write sentences using two words you wrote above.

1. _____

_____

2. _____

_____

Using Context Clues

We can sometimes figure out what a challenging
new word means by reading the rest of the sentence.

> **limber**—bending easily

The gymnast had to be strong
and **limber** to do her routine.

1 Lay out the mats and the cards.

2 Read one sentence on a mat
at a time.

3 Find the word on a card that
correctly completes the sentence.
Place the card on the mat.

4 Complete the response form.

Response Form

Using Context Clues

Look at the completed mats. Write the word you chose next to the number of the sentence.

1.	quizzical	13.	erroneous
2.	extricate	14.	jubilant
3.	perennial	15.	converge
4.	ambiguous	16.	vehement
5.	taunting	17.	utter
6.	flaunt	18.	charisma
7.	fastidious	19.	shallow
8.	benefactor	20.	sanctioned
9.	encumbered	21.	ventilation
10.	mesmerized	22.	luscious
11.	urban	23.	akimbo
12.	cavort	24.	concoct

Write sentences using two words you wrote above.

Answers will vary.

1. _____

2. _____

(fold)

Answer Key

Using Context Clues

Answer Key
Using Context Clues

 A

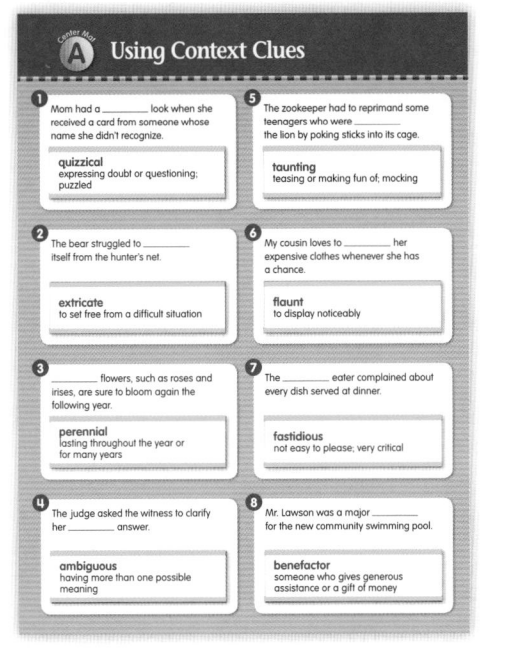

A Using Context Clues

1 Mom had a _____ look when she received a card from someone whose name she didn't recognize.

quizzical
expressing doubt or questioning; puzzled

2 The bear struggled to _____ itself from the hunter's net.

extricate
to set free from a difficult situation

3 _____ flowers, such as roses and irises, are sure to bloom again the following year.

perennial
lasting throughout the year or for many years

4 The judge asked the witness to clarify her _____ answer.

ambiguous
having more than one possible meaning

5 The zookeeper had to reprimand some teenagers who were _____ the lion by poking sticks into its cage.

taunting
teasing or making fun of; mocking

6 My cousin loves to _____ her expensive clothes whenever she has a chance.

flaunt
to display noticeably

7 The _____ eater complained about every dish served at dinner.

fastidious
not easy to please; very critical

8 Mr. Lawson was a major _____ for the new community swimming pool.

benefactor
someone who gives generous assistance or a gift of money

B

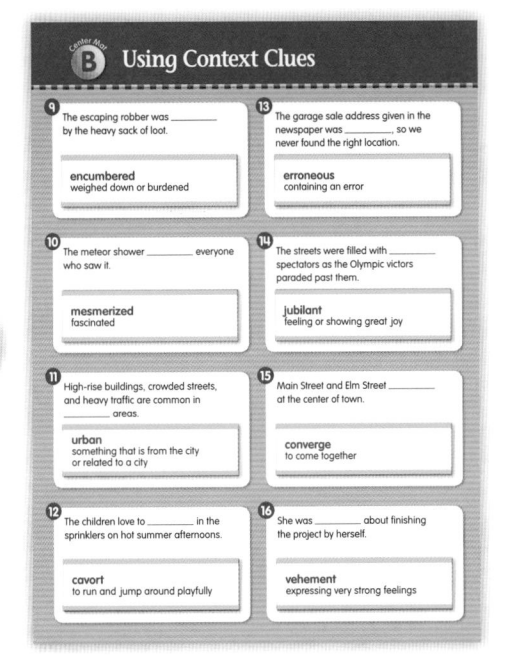

B Using Context Clues

9 The escaping robber was _____ by the heavy sack of loot.

encumbered
weighed down or burdened

10 The meteor shower _____ everyone who saw it.

mesmerized
fascinated

11 High-rise buildings, crowded streets, and heavy traffic are common in _____ areas.

urban
something that is from the city or related to a city

12 The children love to _____ in the sprinklers on hot summer afternoons.

cavort
to run and jump around playfully

13 The garage sale address given in the newspaper was _____, so we never found the right location.

erroneous
containing an error

14 The streets were filled with _____ spectators as the Olympic victors paraded past them.

jubilant
feeling or showing great joy

15 Main Street and Elm Street _____ at the center of town.

converge
to come together

16 She was _____ about finishing the project by herself.

vehement
expressing very strong feelings

C

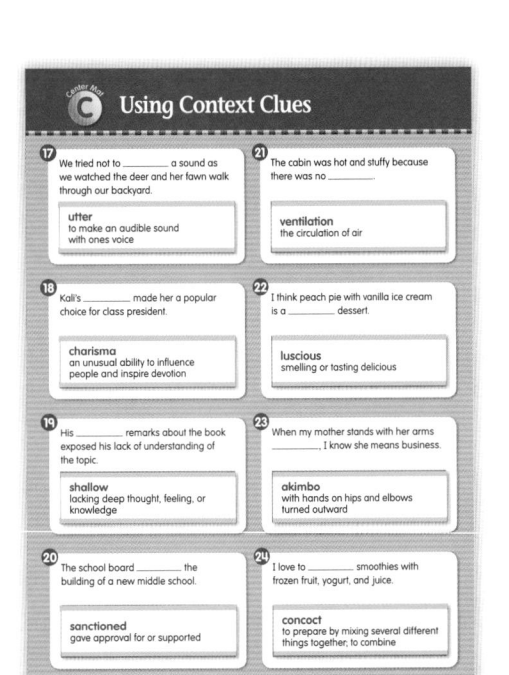

C Using Context Clues

17 We tried not to _____ a sound as we watched the deer and her fawn walk through our backyard.

utter
to make an audible sound with ones voice

18 Kali's _____ made her a popular choice for class president.

charisma
an unusual ability to influence people and inspire devotion

19 His _____ remarks about the book exposed his lack of understanding of the topic.

shallow
lacking deep thought, feeling, or knowledge

20 The school board _____ the building of a new middle school.

sanctioned
gave approval for or supported

21 The cabin was hot and stuffy because there was no _____.

ventilation
the circulation of air

22 I think peach pie with vanilla ice cream is a _____ dessert.

luscious
smelling or tasting delicious

23 When my mother stands with her arms _____, I know she means business.

akimbo
with hands on hips and elbows turned outward

24 I love to _____ smoothies with frozen fruit, yogurt, and juice.

concoct
to prepare by mixing several different things together; to combine

1 Mom had a _____ look when she received a card from someone whose name she didn't recognize.

5 The zookeeper had to reprimand some teenagers who were _____ the lion by poking sticks into its cage.

2 The bear struggled to _____ itself from the hunter's net.

6 My cousin loves to _____ her expensive clothes whenever she has a chance.

3 _____ flowers, such as roses and irises, are sure to bloom again the following year.

7 The _____ eater complained about every dish served at dinner.

4 The judge asked the witness to clarify her _____ answer.

8 Mr. Lawson was a major _____ for the new community swimming pool.

9 The escaping robber was _____ by the heavy sack of loot.

13 The garage sale address given in the newspaper was _____, so we never found the right location.

10 The meteor shower _____ everyone who saw it.

14 The streets were filled with _____ spectators as the Olympic victors paraded past them.

11 High-rise buildings, crowded streets, and heavy traffic are common in _____ areas.

15 Main Street and Elm Street _____ at the center of town.

12 The children love to _____ in the sprinklers on hot summer afternoons.

16 She was _____ about finishing the project by herself.

Take It to Your Seat Centers—Reading & Language • EMC 2846 • © Evan-Moor Corp.

17 We tried not to _____ a sound as we watched the deer and her fawn walk through our backyard.

18 Kali's _____ made her a popular choice for class president.

19 His _____ remarks about the book exposed his lack of understanding of the topic.

20 The school board _____ the building of a new middle school.

21 The cabin was hot and stuffy because there was no _____.

22 I think peach pie with vanilla ice cream is a _____ dessert.

23 When my mother stands with her arms _____, I know she means business.

24 I love to _____ smoothies with frozen fruit, yogurt, and juice.

quizzical expressing doubt or questioning; puzzled	**extricate** to set free from a difficult situation
flaunt to display noticeably	**taunting** teasing or making fun of; mocking
ambiguous having more than one possible meaning	**fastidious** not easy to please; very critical
	perennial lasting throughout the year or for many years
erroneous containing an error	**encumbered** weighed down or burdened
	benefactor someone who gives generous assistance or a gift of money
urban something that is from the city or related to a city	**mesmerized** fascinated
	jubilant feeling or showing great joy
vehement expressing very strong feelings	**converge** to come together
	cavort to run and jump around playfully
charisma an unusual ability to influence people and inspire devotion	**utter** to make an audible sound with ones voice
	ventilation the circulation of air
akimbo with hands on hips and elbows turned outward	**luscious** smelling or tasting delicious
	shallow lacking deep thought, feeling, or knowledge
	sanctioned gave approval for or supported
	concoct to prepare by mixing several different things together; to combine

Using Context Clues

Take It to Your Seat Centers—Reading & Language

EMC 2846 • © Evan-Moor Corp.

Using Context Clues

Take It to Your Seat Centers—Reading & Language

EMC 2846 • © Evan-Moor Corp.

Using Context Clues

Take It to Your Seat Centers—Reading & Language

EMC 2846 • © Evan-Moor Corp.

Using Context Clues

Take It to Your Seat Centers—Reading & Language

EMC 2846 • © Evan-Moor Corp.

Using Context Clues

Take It to Your Seat Centers—Reading & Language

EMC 2846 • © Evan-Moor Corp.

Using Context Clues

Take It to Your Seat Centers—Reading & Language

EMC 2846 • © Evan-Moor Corp.

Using Context Clues

Take It to Your Seat Centers—Reading & Language

EMC 2846 • © Evan-Moor Corp.

Using Context Clues

Take It to Your Seat Centers—Reading & Language

EMC 2846 • © Evan-Moor Corp.

Using Context Clues

Take It to Your Seat Centers—Reading & Language

EMC 2846 • © Evan-Moor Corp.

Using Context Clues

Take It to Your Seat Centers—Reading & Language

EMC 2846 • © Evan-Moor Corp.

Using Context Clues

Take It to Your Seat Centers—Reading & Language

EMC 2846 • © Evan-Moor Corp.

Using Context Clues

Take It to Your Seat Centers—Reading & Language

EMC 2846 • © Evan-Moor Corp.

Using Context Clues

Take It to Your Seat Centers—Reading & Language

EMC 2846 • © Evan-Moor Corp.

Using Context Clues

Take It to Your Seat Centers—Reading & Language

EMC 2846 • © Evan-Moor Corp.

Using Context Clues

Take It to Your Seat Centers—Reading & Language

EMC 2846 • © Evan-Moor Corp.

Using Context Clues

Take It to Your Seat Centers—Reading & Language

EMC 2846 • © Evan-Moor Corp.

Using Context Clues

Take It to Your Seat Centers—Reading & Language

EMC 2846 • © Evan-Moor Corp.

Using Context Clues

Take It to Your Seat Centers—Reading & Language

EMC 2846 • © Evan-Moor Corp.

Using Context Clues

Take It to Your Seat Centers—Reading & Language

EMC 2846 • © Evan-Moor Corp.

Using Context Clues

Take It to Your Seat Centers—Reading & Language

EMC 2846 • © Evan-Moor Corp.

Inference

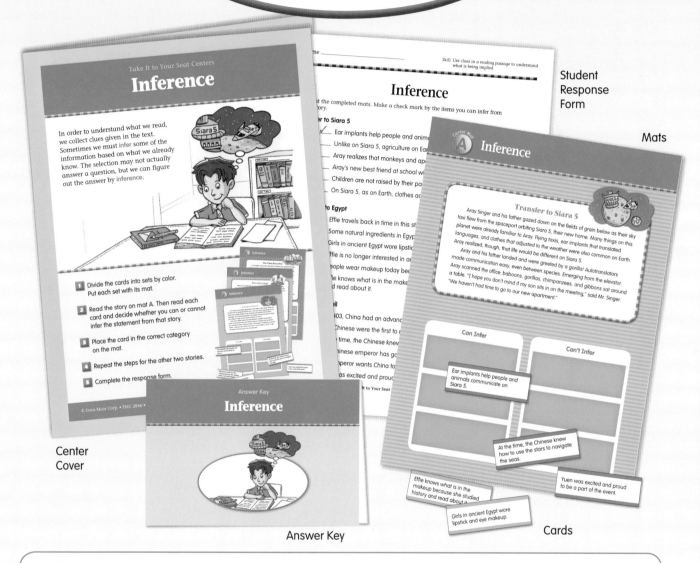

Student Response Form

Mats

Center Cover

Answer Key

Cards

Skill
Use clues in a reading passage to understand what is being implied

Prepare the Center
Follow the directions on page 3.

Introduce the Center
Demonstrate how the center works. State the goal: *You will read each story and the cards that go with it, decide which statements can be inferred from the story and which cannot, and then place the cards in the correct categories on the mats.*

Name _____

Skill: Use clues in a reading passage to understand
what is being implied

Inference

Look at the completed mats. Make a check mark by the items you can infer from each story.

Transfer to Siara 5

✓ Ear implants help people and animals communicate on Siara 5.

_____ Unlike on Siara 5, agriculture on Earth is mostly automated.

_____ Aray realizes that monkeys and apes work in offices on Siara.

_____ Aray's new best friend at school will be a chimpanzee.

_____ Children are not raised by their parents on future Earth.

_____ On Siara 5, as on Earth, clothes adjust to the planet's weather.

Effie's Visit to Egypt

_____ Effie travels back in time in this story.

_____ Some natural ingredients in Egyptian makeup were harmful.

_____ Girls in ancient Egypt wore lipstick and eye makeup.

_____ Effie is no longer interested in archaeology when she wakes up.

_____ People wear makeup today because the Egyptians did.

_____ Effie knows what is in the makeup because she studied history and read about it.

The Fleet Sets Sail

_____ In 1403, China had an advanced culture.

_____ The Chinese were the first to name the stars.

_____ At the time, the Chinese knew how to use the stars to navigate the seas.

_____ The Chinese emperor has gained the power through fighting wars.

_____ The emperor wants China to be a world leader.

_____ Yuen was excited and proud to be a part of the event.

136 Response Form   Take It to Your Seat Centers—Reading & Language • EMC 2846 • © Evan-Moor Corp.

Inference

In order to understand what we read, we collect clues given in the text. Sometimes we must **infer** some of the information based on what we already know. The selection may not actually answer a question, but we can figure out the answer by **inference**.

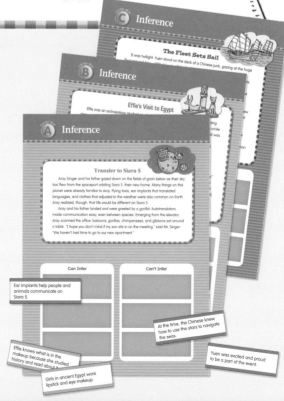

1. Divide the cards into sets by color. Put each set with its mat.

2. Read the story on mat A. Then read each card and decide whether you can or cannot infer the statement from that story.

3. Place the card in the correct category on the mat.

4. Repeat the steps for the other two stories.

5. Complete the response form.

Inference

Answer Key

(fold)

Response Form

Inference

Look at the completed mats. Make a check mark by the items you can infer from each story.

Transfer to Siara 5

✓ Ear implants help people and animals communicate on Siara 5.

____ Unlike on Siara 5, agriculture on Earth is mostly automated.

✓ Aray realizes that monkeys and apes work in offices on Siara.

____ Aray's new best friend at school will be a chimpanzee.

____ Children are not raised by their parents on future Earth.

✓ On Siara 5, as on Earth, clothes adjust to the planet's weather.

Effie's Visit to Egypt

✓ Effie travels back in time in this story.

✓ Some natural ingredients in Egyptian makeup were harmful.

____ Girls in ancient Egypt wore lipstick and eye makeup.

____ Effie is no longer interested in archaeology when she wakes up.

____ People wear makeup today because the Egyptians did.

✓ Effie knows what is in the makeup because she studied history and read about it.

The Fleet Sets Sail

✓ In 1403, China had an advanced culture.

____ The Chinese were the first to name the stars.

✓ At the time, the Chinese knew how to use the stars to navigate the seas.

____ The Chinese emperor has gained the power through fighting wars.

✓ The emperor wants China to be a world leader.

____ Yuen was excited and proud to be a part of the event.

Take It to Your Seat Centers—Reading & Language • EMC 2846 • © Evan-Moor Corp.

Answer Key

Inference

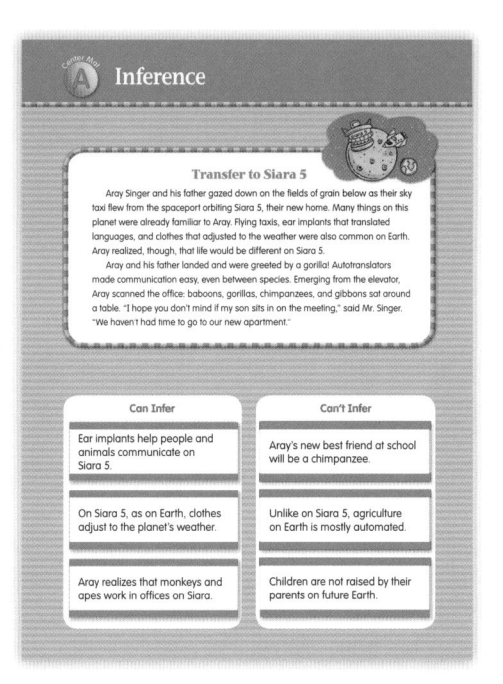

Transfer to Siara 5

Aray Singer and his father gazed down on the fields of grain below as their sky taxi flew from the spaceport orbiting Siara 5, their new home. Many things on this planet were already familiar to Aray. Flying taxis, ear implants that translated languages, and clothes that adjusted to the weather were also common on Earth. Aray realized, though, that life would be different on Siara 5.

Aray and his father landed and were greeted by a gorilla! Autotranslators made communication easy, even between species. Emerging from the elevator, Aray scanned the office: baboons, gorillas, chimpanzees, and gibbons sat around a table. "I hope you don't mind if my son sits in on the meeting," said Mr. Singer. "We haven't had time to go to our new apartment."

Can Infer	Can't Infer
Ear implants help people and animals communicate on Siara 5.	Aray's new best friend at school will be a chimpanzee.
On Siara 5, as on Earth, clothes adjust to the planet's weather.	Unlike on Siara 5, agriculture on Earth is mostly automated.
Aray realizes that monkeys and apes work in offices on Siara.	Children are not raised by their parents on future Earth.

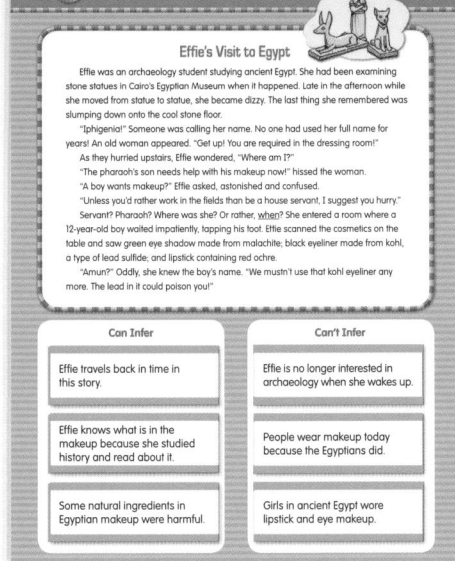

Effie's Visit to Egypt

Effie was an archaeology student studying ancient Egypt. She had been examining stone statues in Cairo's Egyptian Museum when it happened. Late in the afternoon while she moved from statue to statue, she became dizzy. The last thing she remembered was slumping down onto the cool stone floor.

"Iphigenia!" Someone was calling her name. No one had used her full name for years! An old woman appeared. "Get up! You are required in the dressing room!"

As they hurried upstairs, Effie wondered, "Where am I?"

"The pharaoh's son needs help with his makeup now!" hissed the woman.

"A boy wants makeup?" Effie asked, astonished and confused.

"Unless you'd rather work in the fields than be a house servant, I suggest you hurry." Servant? Pharaoh? Where was she? Or rather, _when_? She entered a room where a 12-year-old boy waited impatiently, tapping his foot. Effie scanned the cosmetics on the table and saw green eye shadow made from malachite; black eyeliner made from kohl, a type of lead sulfide; and lipstick containing red ochre.

"Amun?" Oddly, she knew the boy's name. "We mustn't use that kohl eyeliner any more. The lead in it could poison you!"

Can Infer	Can't Infer
Effie travels back in time in this story.	Effie is no longer interested in archaeology when she wakes up.
Effie knows what is in the makeup because she studied history and read about it.	People wear makeup today because the Egyptians did.
Some natural ingredients in Egyptian makeup were harmful.	Girls in ancient Egypt wore lipstick and eye makeup.

The Fleet Sets Sail

It was twilight. Yuen stood on the deck of a Chinese junk, gazing at the huge fleet around him—300 ships in all, he had been told. Too many to see in the growing dark, there were supply ships, battleships, horse transports, and more. Most had 9 masts and 12 sails. Many were more than 450 feet long.

The year was 1403. Thousands of people had lined the Yangtze River to see the armada off that morning. Yuen was only a simple deckhand, ignorant of the fact that he was part of an event unlike anything that had come before it.

Yuen was not yet fully grown. What did he know of the fleet's goals? He knew only this that this was to be a trading mission. Beyond that? Some said the emperor had directed Admiral Zheng He to forge alliances, collect exotic animals, and persuade rulers to pay tribute to China. Others believed the admiral's job was much more than that—to explore civilizations at the ends of the earth, however far away they might be.

As stars began to appear, Yuen took a bite of pickled fruit and watched a man take out a strange instrument. The man seemed to be measuring the stars.

Can Infer	Can't Infer
In 1403, China had an advanced culture.	Yuen was excited and proud to be a part of the event.
The emperor wants China to be a world leader.	The Chinese emperor has gained the power through fighting wars.
At the time, the Chinese knew how to use the stars to navigate the seas.	The Chinese were the first to name the stars.

Inference

Transfer to Siara 5

Aray Singer and his father gazed down on the fields of grain below as their sky taxi flew from the spaceport orbiting Siara 5, their new home. Many things on this planet were already familiar to Aray. Flying taxis, ear implants that translated languages, and clothes that adjusted to the weather were also common on Earth. Aray realized, though, that life would be different on Siara 5.

Aray and his father landed and were greeted by a gorilla! Autotranslators made communication easy, even between species. Emerging from the elevator, Aray scanned the office: baboons, gorillas, chimpanzees, and gibbons sat around a table. "I hope you don't mind if my son sits in on the meeting," said Mr. Singer. "We haven't had time to go to our new apartment."

Can Infer	Can't Infer

Inference

Effie's Visit to Egypt

Effie was an archaeology student studying ancient Egypt. She had been examining stone statues in Cairo's Egyptian Museum when it happened. Late in the afternoon while she moved from statue to statue, she became dizzy. The last thing she remembered was slumping down onto the cool stone floor.

"Iphigenia!" Someone was calling her name. No one had used her full name for years! An old woman appeared. "Get up! You are required in the dressing room!"

As they hurried upstairs, Effie wondered, "Where am I?"

"The pharaoh's son needs help with his makeup now!" hissed the woman.

"A boy wants makeup?" Effie asked, astonished and confused.

"Unless you'd rather work in the fields than be a house servant, I suggest you hurry."

Servant? Pharaoh? Where was she? Or rather, <u>when</u>? She entered a room where a 12-year-old boy waited impatiently, tapping his foot. Effie scanned the cosmetics on the table and saw green eye shadow made from malachite; black eyeliner made from kohl, a type of lead sulfide; and lipstick containing red ochre.

"Amun?" Oddly, she knew the boy's name. "We mustn't use that kohl eyeliner any more. The lead in it could poison you!"

Can Infer	Can't Infer

Take It to Your Seat Centers—Reading & Language • EMC 2846 • © Evan-Moor Corp.

Inference

The Fleet Sets Sail

It was twilight. Yuen stood on the deck of a Chinese junk, gazing at the huge fleet around him—300 ships in all, he had been told. Too many to see in the growing dark, there were supply ships, battleships, horse transports, and more. Most had 9 masts and 12 sails. Many were more than 450 feet long.

The year was 1403. Thousands of people had lined the Yangtze River to see the armada off that morning. Yuen was only a simple deckhand, ignorant of the fact that he was part of an event unlike anything that had come before it.

Yuen was not yet fully grown. What did he know of the fleet's goals? He knew only that this was to be a trading mission. Beyond that? Some said the emperor had directed Admiral Zheng He to forge alliances, collect exotic animals, and persuade rulers to pay tribute to China. Others believed the admiral's job was much more than that—to explore civilizations at the ends of the earth, however far away they might be.

As stars began to appear, Yuen took a bite of pickled fruit and watched a man take out a strange instrument. The man seemed to be measuring the stars.

Can Infer

Can't Infer

Ear implants help people and animals communicate on Siara 5.	Aray's new best friend at school will be a chimpanzee.
Aray realizes that monkeys and apes work in offices on Siara.	Unlike on Siara 5, agriculture on Earth is mostly automated.
On Siara 5, as on Earth, clothes adjust to the planet's weather.	Children are not raised by their parents on future Earth.
Effie travels back in time in this story.	Effie is no longer interested in archaeology when she wakes up.
Effie knows what is in the makeup because she studied history and read about it.	People wear makeup today because the Egyptians did.
Some natural ingredients in Egyptian makeup were harmful.	Girls in ancient Egypt wore lipstick and eye makeup.
In 1403, China had an advanced culture.	Yuen was excited and proud to be a part of the event.
The emperor wants China to be a world leader.	The Chinese emperor has gained the power through fighting wars.
At the time, the Chinese knew how to use the stars to navigate the seas.	The Chinese were the first to name the stars.

Inference

Take It to Your Seat Centers
Reading & Language
EMC 2846 • © Evan-Moor Corp.

Inference

Take It to Your Seat Centers
Reading & Language
EMC 2846 • © Evan-Moor Corp.

Inference

Take It to Your Seat Centers
Reading & Language
EMC 2846 • © Evan-Moor Corp.

Inference

Take It to Your Seat Centers
Reading & Language
EMC 2846 • © Evan-Moor Corp.

Inference

Take It to Your Seat Centers
Reading & Language
EMC 2846 • © Evan-Moor Corp.

Inference

Take It to Your Seat Centers
Reading & Language
EMC 2846 • © Evan-Moor Corp.

Inference

Take It to Your Seat Centers
Reading & Language
EMC 2846 • © Evan-Moor Corp.

Inference

Take It to Your Seat Centers
Reading & Language
EMC 2846 • © Evan-Moor Corp.

Inference

Take It to Your Seat Centers
Reading & Language
EMC 2846 • © Evan-Moor Corp.

Inference

Take It to Your Seat Centers
Reading & Language
EMC 2846 • © Evan-Moor Corp.

Inference

Take It to Your Seat Centers
Reading & Language
EMC 2846 • © Evan-Moor Corp.

Inference

Take It to Your Seat Centers
Reading & Language
EMC 2846 • © Evan-Moor Corp.

Inference

Take It to Your Seat Centers
Reading & Language
EMC 2846 • © Evan-Moor Corp.

Inference

Take It to Your Seat Centers
Reading & Language
EMC 2846 • © Evan-Moor Corp.

Inference

Take It to Your Seat Centers
Reading & Language
EMC 2846 • © Evan-Moor Corp.

Inference

Take It to Your Seat Centers
Reading & Language
EMC 2846 • © Evan-Moor Corp.

Inference

Take It to Your Seat Centers
Reading & Language
EMC 2846 • © Evan-Moor Corp.

Inference

Take It to Your Seat Centers
Reading & Language
EMC 2846 • © Evan-Moor Corp.

Take It to Your Seat Centers

Main Idea and Details

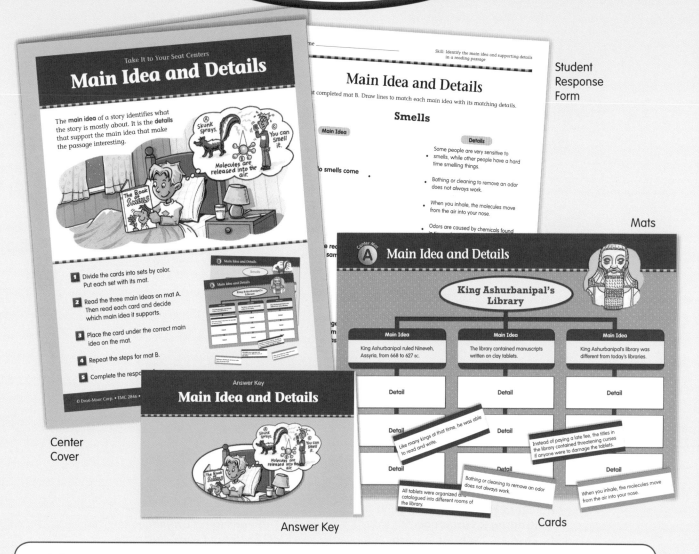

Student Response Form

Center Cover

Answer Key

Mats

Cards

Skill
Identify the main idea and supporting details in a reading passage

Prepare the Center
Follow the directions on page 3.

Introduce the Center
Demonstrate how the center works. State the goal: *You will read the main ideas on each mat and the detail cards that go with them, decide which details support each main idea, and then place the cards on the mat.*

Main Idea and Details

Look at completed mat B. Draw lines to match each main idea with its matching details.

Smells

Main Idea

Details

- Some people are very sensitive to smells, while other people have a hard time smelling things.

Where do smells come from? •

- Bathing or cleaning to remove an odor does not always work.

- When you inhale, the molecules move from the air into your nose.

- Odors are caused by chemicals found in tiny molecules that float in the air.

Not everyone reacts to smells in the same way. •

- The sensitivity to smells is passed on from parents to their children.

- In order to eliminate an unpleasant odor, you must change the chemical makeup of its molecules.

- Sensitivity to smells effects how we behave when faced with strong odors.

- Everything gives off a mix of molecules that determine its smell.

Strong smells linger because the chemicals do not change easily. •

- The odor of skunk spray is an example of a strong smell that is hard to get rid of.

Take It to Your Seat Centers—Reading & Language • EMC 2846 • © Evan-Moor Corp.

Main Idea and Details

The **main idea** of a story identifies what the story is mostly about. It is the **details** that support the main idea that make the passage interesting.

1 Divide the cards into sets by color. Put each set with its mat.

2 Read the three main ideas on mat A. Then read each card and decide which main idea it supports.

3 Place the card under the correct main idea on the mat.

4 Repeat the steps for mat B.

5 Complete the response form.

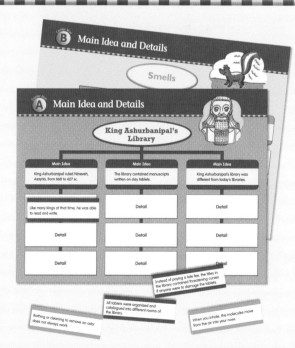

Main Idea and Details

Look at completed mat B. Draw lines to match each main idea with its matching details.

Smells

Main Idea

- Strong smells linger because the chemicals do not change easily.
- Not everyone reacts to smells in the same way.
- Where do smells come from?

Details

- The odor of skunk spray is an example of a strong smell that is hard to get rid of.
- Everything gives off a mix of molecules that determine its smell.
- Sensitivity to smells effects how we behave when faced with strong odors.
- In order to eliminate an unpleasant odor, you must change the chemical makeup of its molecules.
- The sensitivity to smells is passed on from parents to their children.
- Odors are caused by chemicals found in tiny molecules that float in the air.
- When you inhale, the molecules move from the air into your nose.
- Bathing or cleaning to remove an odor does not always work.
- Some people are very sensitive to smells, while other people have a hard time smelling things.

Response Form

(fold)

Answer Key

Main Idea and Details

Main Idea and Details

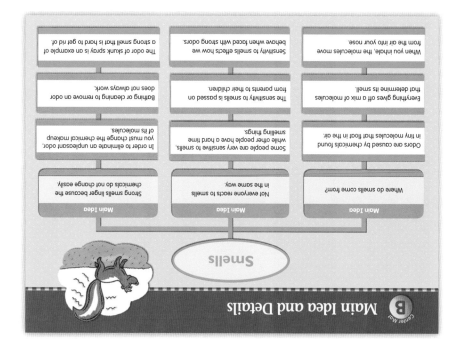

A

Center Mat — **Main Idea and Details**

King Ashurbanipal's Library

Main Idea: King Ashurbanipal ruled Nineveh, Assyria, from 668 to 627 BC.
- Like many kings at that time, he was able to read and write.
- King Ashurbanipal is remembered for starting the first library during his reign.
- Nineveh was an ancient city located near what is now the city of Mosul, Iraq.

Main Idea: The library contained manuscripts written on clay tablets.
- Some of the tablets were taken from defeated enemies during wartime or copied from earlier tablets.
- There were many topics represented: religion, science, magic, and history.
- All tablets were organized and catalogued into different rooms of the library.

Main Idea: King Ashurbanipal's library was different from today's libraries.
- Today, we read books written on paper, not tablets made of clay.
- Instead of paying a late fee, the titles in the library contained threatening curses if anyone were to damage the tablets.
- Today, most libraries are open to everyone, but King Ashurbanipal's library was private and open only to scholars.

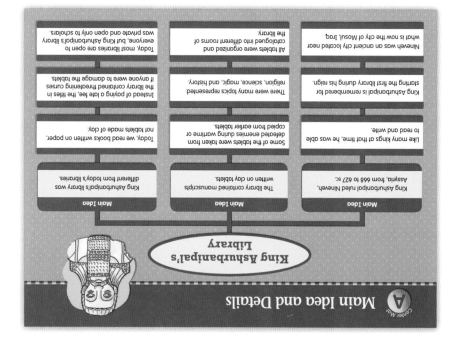

B

Center Mat — **Main Idea and Details**

Smells

Main Idea: Where do smells come from?
- Odors are caused by chemicals found in tiny molecules that float in the air.
- Everything gives off a mix of molecules that determine its smell.
- When you inhale, the molecules move from the air into your nose.

Main Idea: Not everyone reacts to smells in the same way.
- Some people are very sensitive to smells, while other people have a hard time smelling things.
- The sensitivity to smells is passed on from parents to their children.
- Sensitivity to smells effects how we behave when faced with strong odors.

Main Idea: Strong smells linger because the chemicals do not change easily.
- In order to eliminate an unpleasant odor, you must change the chemical makeup of its molecules.
- Bathing or cleaning to remove an odor does not always work.
- The odor of skunk spray is an example of a strong smell that is hard to get rid of.

A

Main Idea and Details

King Ashurbanipal's Library

Main Idea

King Ashurbanipal ruled Nineveh, Assyria, from 668 to 627 BC.

Detail

Detail

Detail

Main Idea

The library contained manuscripts written on clay tablets.

Detail

Detail

Detail

Main Idea

King Ashurbanipal's library was different from today's libraries.

Detail

Detail

Detail

Main Idea and Details

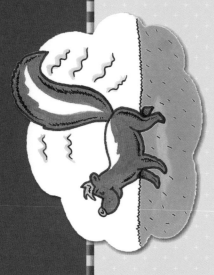

Smells

Main Idea

Where do smells come from?

| Detail |
| Detail |
| Detail |

Main Idea

Not everyone reacts to smells in the same way.

| Detail |
| Detail |
| Detail |

Main Idea

Strong smells linger because the chemicals do not change easily.

| Detail |
| Detail |
| Detail |

Today, we read books written on paper, not tablets made of clay.

Instead of paying a late fee, the titles in the library contained threatening curses if anyone were to damage the tablets.

Today, most libraries are open to everyone, but King Ashurbanipal's library was private and open only to scholars.

In order to eliminate an unpleasant odor, you must change the chemical makeup of its molecules.

Bathing or cleaning to remove an odor does not always work.

The odor of skunk spray is an example of a strong smell that is hard to get rid of.

Some of the tablets were taken from defeated enemies during wartime or copied from earlier tablets.

There were many topics represented: religion, science, magic, and history.

All tablets were organized and catalogued into different rooms of the library.

Some people are very sensitive to smells, while other people have a hard time smelling things.

The sensitivity to smells is passed on from parents to their children.

Sensitivity to smells effects how we behave when faced with strong odors.

Like many kings at that time, he was able to read and write.

King Ashurbanipal is remembered for starting the first library during his reign.

Nineveh was an ancient city located near what is now the city of Mosul, Iraq.

Odors are caused by chemicals found in tiny molecules that float in the air.

Everything gives off a mix of molecules that determine its smell.

When you inhale, the molecules move from the air into your nose.

Main Idea and Details
Take It to Your Seat Centers
Reading & Language
EMC 2846 • © Evan-Moor Corp.

Main Idea and Details
Take It to Your Seat Centers
Reading & Language
EMC 2846 • © Evan-Moor Corp.

Main Idea and Details
Take It to Your Seat Centers
Reading & Language
EMC 2846 • © Evan-Moor Corp.

Main Idea and Details
Take It to Your Seat Centers
Reading & Language
EMC 2846 • © Evan-Moor Corp.

Main Idea and Details
Take It to Your Seat Centers
Reading & Language
EMC 2846 • © Evan-Moor Corp.

Main Idea and Details
Take It to Your Seat Centers
Reading & Language
EMC 2846 • © Evan-Moor Corp.

Main Idea and Details
Take It to Your Seat Centers
Reading & Language
EMC 2846 • © Evan-Moor Corp.

Main Idea and Details
Take It to Your Seat Centers
Reading & Language
EMC 2846 • © Evan-Moor Corp.

Main Idea and Details
Take It to Your Seat Centers
Reading & Language
EMC 2846 • © Evan-Moor Corp.

Main Idea and Details
Take It to Your Seat Centers
Reading & Language
EMC 2846 • © Evan-Moor Corp.

Main Idea and Details
Take It to Your Seat Centers
Reading & Language
EMC 2846 • © Evan-Moor Corp.

Main Idea and Details
Take It to Your Seat Centers
Reading & Language
EMC 2846 • © Evan-Moor Corp.

Main Idea and Details
Take It to Your Seat Centers
Reading & Language
EMC 2846 • © Evan-Moor Corp.

Main Idea and Details
Take It to Your Seat Centers
Reading & Language
EMC 2846 • © Evan-Moor Corp.

Main Idea and Details
Take It to Your Seat Centers
Reading & Language
EMC 2846 • © Evan-Moor Corp.

Main Idea and Details
Take It to Your Seat Centers
Reading & Language
EMC 2846 • © Evan-Moor Corp.

Main Idea and Details
Take It to Your Seat Centers
Reading & Language
EMC 2846 • © Evan-Moor Corp.

Main Idea and Details
Take It to Your Seat Centers
Reading & Language
EMC 2846 • © Evan-Moor Corp.